Pastel portrait of
Pieter Teyler van der Hulst
by Taco Jelgersma

Victoria and Albert Museum

Drawings from the Teyler Museum, Haarlem

Catalogue by
I. Q. van Regteren Altena and
P. W. Ward-Jackson

London 1970

Designed by HMSO/John Saville

Printed for Her Majesty's Stationery Office
by Eyre & Spottiswoode Ltd, Thanet Press, Margate

Dd 646948   4M   3/70

Contents

Foreword

The Teyler Museum at Haarlem, whose history is summarised by Professor van Regteren Altena in the introduction to this catalogue, is one of the oldest in Europe. It houses, among much else, a large collection of old master drawings, which includes a number of magnificent sheets by Michelangelo, Raphael and Rembrandt and some of the most beautiful surviving drawings by Claude Lorrain. None the less, outside the world of specialists in old master drawings, the collection is relatively little known. One reason for this is that only a small part of the collection is regularly exhibited at Haarlem, and another is that, though the Museum has from time to time made generous loans to specialised exhibitions in Holland and abroad, no substantial cross-section of its drawings has ever been exhibited. We regard it, therefore, as a great honour that the Directors of the Teyler Foundation have decided to let us have the only exhibition which the Museum has ever sent outside its walls. The fact that it includes five sheets by Michelangelo, three by Raphael, one by Correggio, seven by Claude Lorrain and four by Rembrandt, testifies to its exceptional importance. That the selection is so rich is due to the generosity of Professor van Regteren Altena, the Curator of the Art Collections, who has spared no pains to make the exhibition possible. We are much indebted to him and to Mr J. H. van Borssum Buisman, the resident curator of the Teyler Museum, for their constant assistance in the preparation of the exhibition and the catalogue. We are also indebted to the Dutch Government for a generous contribution towards meeting the cost of the exhibition and to Mr J. B. Braaksma, Cultural Counsellor at the Royal Netherlands Embassy, for his help.

The catalogue entries for the Dutch and Flemish drawings have been prepared by Professor van Regteren Altena, and those for the Italian and French drawings by Mr P. W. Ward-Jackson, Deputy Keeper of the Department of Prints and Drawings. Mr Ward-Jackson has received valuable assistance from Miss Karin Hartmann, Miss Felice Stampfle, Miss Janet Steen, Dottoressa Luisa Vertova-Nicolson, Mr Jacob Bean, Mr J. A. Gere, Mr Michael Hirst, Mr Michael Kitson and Mr Philip Pouncey. Professor van Regteren Altena is grateful to the Print Room of the Rijksmuseum and its Library, as well as to the Rijksbureau voor Kunsthistorische Documentatie, for the material that they have placed at his disposal.

JOHN POPE-HENNESSY
Director, Victoria and Albert Museum

Introduction

The town of Haarlem, once separated from Amsterdam by a three hours walk between Rembrandt's pastures and the River IJ, but today approached halfway by its towering suburbs, is by origin her elder sister. Before Amsterdam had obtained municipal rights, the Counts of Holland had granted them to Haarlem, and set up there a hall, where they occasionally held court. There is a tradition that their quarters stood on ground now occupied by the Teyler Foundation or very near to it. In the sixteenth century a bishop's see was established in Haarlem, to last for a short time only before the Reformation was officially recognised. The benches in the upper choir of the solid late Gothic church named after St. Bavo still show the coats of arms of the principal noble families of Holland who outlived the Middle Ages. In 1815 Haarlem's historical precedence was once more affirmed by the decision to constitute it the capital of the province of North Holland. Since the fifteenth century Haarlem's rich burghers had not lacked artists, first to adorn their altars, then to paint their portraits, and finally to record the picturesque scenery of the inner dunes which border the town. During the eighteenth century it still competed with its mighty rival in civil occupations devoted to the arts, to letters and to science. With no more war, and fewer reckless adventures and daring enterprises on hand, more contemplative pursuits were adopted. Though not maintaining an Athenaeum as did Amsterdam, Haarlem witnessed the foundation of a learned society two hundred years ago, which is still flourishing; for looking at the moon and the stars was as popular an occupation for the dilettante in those days as collecting works of art, specimens of natural history and books was for those who craved to obtain that outlook on the world and that universal knowledge which everywhere in Western Europe was the eager demand of the century. A shade of omnivorousness cannot be denied to that noble desire.

Pieter Teyler van der Hulst, by profession a silk merchant, being imbued with such aspirations, and lacking descendants to inherit his possessions, left them at his death in 1778 to found an institution for the advancement of theology, science, the arts and philanthropy. As a liberal Mennonite he wanted it to remain in the hands of fellow citizens thinking on the same rational lines as he did. Teyler was ultimately of English extraction, but the family had lived at Haarlem ever since 1580, when Thomas Teyler at the age of eighteen had fled his country for reasons of religious conviction and settled in Haarlem. Pieter Teyler was his direct descendant. His will mentions the institution of two learned societies and of a museum in which his collections should be shown appropriately. Up to the present day this foundation, headed by five co-opted directors, has been active as an independent body pursuing the ends laid down in Pieter Teyler's almost prophetic last will.

What the contents of his own collections were we are unhappily unable to say. Not the slightest document regarding them has been preserved. However, the more we learn about the subsequent flow of acquisitions, starting in 1779 and continuing up to the present day, the more clear does it become that his share in the present collections must have been of relative importance only. He must have owned a library containing editions of the classical authors and the church fathers; he must also have had a part of the brilliant collection of coins and medals, and a number of prints and drawings kept in volumes, as his pastel portrait by T. H. Jelgersma (frontispiece) shows them lying on the shelves of the cupboard before which he poses. But the collection of scientific instruments which was soon to fill the beautifully constructed oval room, the most conspicuous architectural feature of the growing complex of buildings, was bought by, or made for Doctor Marinus van Marum, the versatile scholar who acted as 'spiritus rector' during the first decades of the Museum's existence. The rich palaeontological collection as well as the minerals seem also to have entered the collection after Teyler's death. Pictures were not bought systematically before the nineteenth century. We may conclude from this that only a part of the library and of the prints, drawings, and coins and medals, and perhaps some specimens of natural history were brought together by Pieter Teyler himself.

Three sections of the collection of prints deserve to be mentioned particularly. Teyler may or may not have possessed some Rembrandts, but the wonderful Rembrandt collection now in the Museum was mainly built up by a series of purchases from the most important sales of the nineteenth century. On the other hand the Adriaen van Ostade collection, also one of the best in existence, was bought as a whole. The Amsterdam collector Jan Danser Nijman had assembled so many prints by Ostade, that they constituted three complete sets of his oeuvre. At his sale the choicest pieces were sold in lot 10, which the Foundation was happy to secure for itself. The third exceptional feature, a large collection of engravings after the work of Rubens, is due to the activity of one of the directors, C. G. Voorhelm Schneevoogt, who collected them all over Europe and finally in 1873 published a catalogue of the subject, a compendium used still by Rubens scholars. Pieter Teyler may be supposed to have had some kind of predilection for old master drawings, because the first keepers of the art collection, Vincent Jansz. van der Vinne (1778-85), who was a personal friend, and Wybrand Hendriks (1785-1819) immediately started buying them. They lived in Teyler's former house, to which it soon became necessary to add new rooms to contain the museum and the library. Their title was that of 'Kasteleyn en opzicheter', that is 'Warden, or host, and surveyor'. The tradition of hospitality expressed in the title has never been lost in that house.

Considering the prices of drawings and other works of art at the time, the resources of the foundation must at first have seemed unlimited. In 1790 it was possible to acquire in Rome from the Duke of Bracciano part of the collection of Italian drawings kept almost intact since Christina, Queen of Sweden, who had sought refuge there as a Catholic convert, bequeathed them to Cardinal Azzolino. From Azzolino's nephew they had been acquired by the Odescalchi, one of whom, the Duke of Bracciano, sold them to Mr Lestevenon, who represented the Teyler Foundation in Rome during the transactions. His request for ten thousand guilders to reimburse himself for the purchase price is one of the few authentic documents preserved on the early history of the art collections. By one stroke the Museum now possessed whole sets of original drawings by Raphael and Michelangelo and by many of the great Italian masters of the sixteenth and seventeenth century. It must be taken for granted that the set of folio drawings sketched by Hendrick Goltzius after antique sculptures, when staying in Rome in 1590, also came from the same source. They had come to the Queen as crown property, since they belonged to the core of the art treasures of the Emperor Rudolph II, chosen by

Koenigsmark to be sent to Stockholm after Prague had capitulated to his arms. It is probable, though not certain, that the album containing a matchless set of drawings by Claude Lorrain from all the different periods of his career was also included in the same purchase.

The provenance of the other French drawings, not numerous but of high quality, is less well known and we do not know the history of the several Watteaus, only one of which bears a collector's stamp: that of Huquier. These may have come to Holland at an early date, but how they came into the collections at Haarlem has not been recorded.

The majority of the drawings in the Museum, those of the Netherlands school, were by no means bought *en bloc*, but accumulated by degrees. Only once before in the history of collecting has a selection of drawings so completely representative of that school been assembled together by a single collector: and that was by Cornelis Ploos van Amstel (1726-98). Active in this field for more than fifty years, this Amsterdam broker had amassed so many drawings of the past and the present, that the albums containing them numbered four times the alphabet from A up to UUUU. The second keeper of the Teyler Museum, Wybrand Hendriks, was present at the sale, where he acquired several items. This was not an exceptional step, as the foundation was represented regularly at the auctions held during the nineteenth century and so took advantage of these chances to fill the lacunae in its collections. As a matter of fact the number, the diversity and the charm of this part of the collection in its present state is mainly due to this continuous response to the opportunities that arose, as well as to the fact that the keepers, according to the rules laid down in Teyler's will, were chosen from the profession of artists, and soon began to supplement their innate taste by learning from the ever increasing collection they had daily under their eyes. One by one the Rembrandts, the Ruysdaels, the van Goyens were chosen from the harvest of former owners, whose names still figure in the numerous sale catalogues, keeping the memory of their achievements alive: Jacob de Vos Senior, Goll van Franckenstein, Isendoorn à Blois, Verstolk van Soelen, Jacob de Vos Junior and many others. The longevity of the foundation did the rest, enabling the process of accumulation to go on continuously, whereas private collections, however old, are apt to be dispersed sooner or later.

Among the keepers two ought to be mentioned especially: Wybrand Hendriks, who seems to have done so much of the earlier mounting and distribution in the portfolios; and H. J. Scholten (1863-1907), who wrote the catalogue of the drawings of the French, German and Netherlandish schools, which is still in use, though unfortunately out of print.

To us present-day onlookers there is nothing surprising in the pace at which museums develop. Pieter Teyler, however, founded an institution of a type which before him only sovereigns had brought into existence, and which they seldom considered primarily as serving the general benefit. It is sad to think that the very antiquity of such a museum is a disadvantage to it today, now that governments and city councils, with public money at their disposal, have taken over the running of museums. To keep going, institutions like the Teyler Foundation need private donations, for which the time seems to have passed. Moreover the prices of old master drawings, if we compare the actual sums spent in guilders, have multiplied a hundred, or rather a thousand times, since the eighteenth century.

Since the first Rembrandt exhibition, held in 1898, the Foundation has lent various objects to exhibitions held in the Netherlands and abroad. Never, however, has an exhibition entirely drawn from its own art collection been held outside the Museum, and the present show will remain an exception to the rule. The excellent condition in which the drawings have been preserved through storing them between the leaves of the traditional 'kunstboeken' or albums should be maintained and might suffer irreparable damage if the drawings were exposed too often to changes of climate.

The choice of the present exhibition has been dictated by the wish to give an impression of the diversity of the collection and of the quality of the drawings. Scholarly interest and completeness have not been aimed at so much as the real pleasure which an educated public may get from what we consider a good drawing. We at the Teyler Museum are grateful to the Director and staff of the Victoria and Albert Museum for their help in organising the exhibition. We owe special thanks to Mr P. W. Ward-Jackson for his valuable contribution to the study of the Italian and French drawings exhibited.

I. Q. VAN REGTEREN ALTENA

Catalogue

The drawings are arranged as far as possible in chronological order. The measurements are expressed in millimetres, first the height, then the width. The paper is white unless otherwise described. There is a list of bibliographical abbreviations on pp. 77-9 and a list of exhibitions referred to in an abbreviated form on p. 81.

Dutch drawings

Paulus Bril

Painter and etcher-engraver. Born Antwerp, 1554; died Rome, 1626.

1 Italian landscape with a hunter shooting duck from a boat, and a country house among trees. Inscribed on the verso *Paulo Brilli*.
Pen and brush with black and brown ink, 202 × 289 mm.
Inv. no. O.2
Provenance From an Italian collection, possibly Queen Christina etc. (see p. 9).
Bibliography Scholten, p. 61, O.2; A. Mayer, *Das Leben und die Werke der Brüder Matthäus und Paul Bril*, Leipzig, 1910, p. 78 (dated c. 1615).

Like most drawings by Paul Bril this is an invented landscape, not drawn from nature. It belongs to a late phase in Bril's career, since he may have learned from Callot the effects to be obtained from heavy brush work to bind entire planes of the scene together, a device which becomes visible in Bril's work from about 1615. A drawing in the Louvre (L.425) of 1623 shows that after that Bril reached a further stage, when he began to approach the manner of the young Claude Lorrain. The present drawing may have belonged to the landscapes acquired at Rome by Queen Christina of Sweden.

Hendrick Goltzius

Engraver and painter. Born Mühlbracht, 1558; died Haarlem, 1616.

2 Portrait of Jacob Matham as a boy of thirteen. Inscribed by the artist *A E 13*. An inscription on the verso is covered by a lining paper.
Metalpoint on prepared yellow coloured paper, 96 × 61 mm.
Inv. no. N.48
Provenance C. Ploos van Amstel, sale 3 March 1800, UU.38, bought for fl. 17.10 by Hendriks for the Teyler Foundation.
Exhibitions Goltzius, Rotterdam-Haarlem, 1958 no. 66, plate 36; Washington, etc., 1958–59, no. 27.
Bibliography Scholten, pp. 44–5, N.48; N. S. Trivas in the *Connoisseur*, Vol. 103, 1939, pp. 212–13, plate 9; Reznicek, Vol. 1, p. 413, no. 377, and Vol. 2, plate 38.

The identity of the sitter has been a matter of dispute, but it seems safe to identify him as the young Jacob Matham, who had become Goltzius's stepson in 1579, and who was thirteen years old in 1584–85. The portrait was bought under that name by Hendriks for the Teyler Foundation in 1800.

It was not acquired, as Reznicek states, from W. P. Kops as a portrait of Hugo Grotius, nor did it belong to the collection of poets' portraits known as *Panpoeticon Batavum* formed by Kops. The so-called Grotius portrait is in oils on paper. The connection with the portrait of a boy in Reznicek 385 (Lugt Collection), inscribed *aet 11. a.° 1583*, is much closer than the connection suggested by Reznicek with Reznicek 376 (in Berlin), which is inscribed *aet. XIII a.° 1586*. In the latter case the boy is differently dressed and too young. Matham was born 15 October, 1571, which fits Reznicek 385.

3 Saint Cecilia, playing the organ, with two singing angels. Signed with the monogram *H G*.
Pen and brush with brownish ink and watercolour, heightened with white on greyish paper. 273 × 188 mm.
Inv. no. N.71
Provenance Probably the Emperor Rudolph II; captured by the Swedes; Queen Christina, etc. (see p. 9).
Exhibitions Amsterdam, 1955, no. 198; Goltzius, Rotterdam-Haarlem, 1958, no. 35, plate 76.
Bibliography Scholten, p. 52, N.71; Reznicek, Vol. 1, pp. 258–59, no. 72, and Vol. 2, plate 104.

An example of Goltzius's early mannerist style from the years immediately preceding his journey to Rome (1587–89). The drawing may have inspired J. de Gheyn for his same subject, engraved by Z. Dolendo (Hollstein 45).

4 Antique marble candelabrum in Santa Costanza, Rome.
Red chalk, 420 × 240 mm (rounded off at the top afterwards).
Inv. no. N.33

Provenance The Emperor Rudolph II, Prague; captured by the Swedes; Queen Christina, etc. (see p. 9).
Bibliography Scholten, p. 42, N.33; Reznicek, Vol. 1, p. 321, no. 200, and Vol. 2, plate 153; I. Q. van Regteren Altena, *Vereeuwigde Stad*, Amsterdam, 1964, p. 102, no. 34, plate 2.

During his stay in Rome Goltzius made a matchless set of drawings after antique sculpture. This one represents one of the three candelabra (now in the Vatican) which the Emperor Constantine had placed in the Mausoleum of his two daughters, afterwards the church of S. Costanza. This candelabrum afterwards stood for a long time in the adjoining Sant' Agnese. The two genii in the margins are from the hidden sides of the tripod. In the background the medieval ambo (pulpit), which is no longer in existence.

5 A landscape of huge mountains with a road winding up and disappearing into a tunnel. Signed with the monogram *H G* and dated *A°/1594*. Inscribed on the verso *N° G*.
Pen and brown ink, 439 × 356 mm.
Inv. no. N.75
Provenance Probably the Emperor Rudolph II; captured by the Swedes; Queen Christina, etc. (see p. 9).
Exhibitions Amsterdam, 1955, no. 199, plate 52; Goltzius, Rotterdam-Haarlem, 1958, no. 83, plate 59.
Bibliography Scholten, p. 53, N.75; Reznicek, Vol. 1, p. 426, no. 396 (with complete literature), and Vol. 2, plate 239.

Reznicek denies the influence of Muziano, as supposed by van Gelder, and instead of that finds in Goltzius an ambition to compete with Pieter Brueghel's pen landscapes.

Hendrick Goltzius

Abraham Bloemaert

Jacques de Gheyn

6 A nude woman seated on a draped cloth. Signed with the monogram *H G* and dated *A° 99.*
Red chalk, 151 × 130 mm.
Inv. no. K.II.107
Exhibitions Goltzius, Rotterdam-Haarlem, 1958, no. 76.
Bibliography Not described by Scholten; Reznicek, Vol. 1, p. 453, no. 434, and Vol. 2, plate 335.

Reznicek shows that this sheet belongs to a group of studies from the nude executed towards 1600 and suggests that Goltzius drew them in preparation for mythological scenes.

Abraham Bloemaert

Painter and engraver. Born Gorkum, 1564; died Utrecht, 1651.

7 A sluice in a ditch with two trees standing beside it.
Black chalk, pen and watercolour, 155 × 196 mm.
Inv. no. O.13
Provenance C. Ploos van Amstel (Lugt 3002 and 3004), sale 3 March 1800, 0.33, bought for fl. 7. – by W. Hendriks for the Teyler Foundation.
Exhibitions Washington, etc., 1958–59, pp. 23–4, no. 36.
Bibliography Scholten, p. 63, O.13; C. Müller-Hofstede, 'Abraham Bloemaert als Landschaftsmaler' in *Oud Holland*, Vol. 44, 1944, p. 193.

Among the many landscapes made by Bloemaert during the first quarter of the seventeenth century based entirely on real scenes in nature, this is one of the most elaborate and seems to be an embellished repetition of a lost sketch from nature.
On the verso Part of a landscape, mostly cut away.

Jacques de Gheyn

Engraver and painter. Born Antwerp, 1565; died at The Hague, 1629.

8 An elderly man, seated, his head bent in a thoughtful mood.
Black chalk on buff paper, 165 × 100 mm.
Inv. no. N.86
Provenance J. van der Marck, sale 29 November 1773, no. 1843 (as one of two portraits of himself); C. Ploos van Amstel (Lugt 3002 and 3004), sale 3 March 1800, with its pendant, also in the Teyler Museum, probably L.9, sold with L.9 to W. P. Kops for fl. 26.–; W. P. Kops, sale 14 March 1808, R8 (both) sold for fl. 20.–to J. de Vos Sr. (not in his sale); Baron J. G. Verstolk van Soelen, sale 22 March 1847, no. 191, sold for fl. 40.–to Michaelis for the Teyler Foundation.
Exhibitions Washington, etc., 1958–59, no. 35.
Bibliography Scholten, p. 56, N.86; Buisman, p. 5, plate 3; I. Q. van Regteren Altena, *The Drawings of Jacques de Gheyn*, Amsterdam, 1936, pp. 47–8.

The same man is portrayed in profile on the companion sheet, which has always changed hands with the present drawing. Furthermore,

Jacques de Gheyn

Jan Brueghel, the Elder

Attributed to Sir Peter Paul Rubens

Follower of Sir Peter Paul Rubens

the profile occurs on a sheet of sketches which came with the Koenigs Collection to the Boymans Museum, Rotterdam (discussed by van Regteren Altena, *op. cit.*). Our attempts to identify the sitter so far have remained without result. A self-portrait seems to be excluded.

Jan Brueghel, the Elder

Painter and etcher. Born Brussels, 1568; died Antwerp, 1625.

9 Sailing boats on a canal with a windmill on the left. Signed *J. Brueghel*.
Pen with brown ink and watercolour, 125 × 200 mm.
Inv. no. 0.6
Provenance C. Ploos van Amstel, sale 3 March 1800, perhaps L.24, sold for fl. 12.– to IJver.
Bibliography Scholten, p. 61, 0.6.

To judge from the neat penwork, it should be dated in the first decade of the seventeenth century.

Attributed to Sir Peter Paul Rubens

Painter. Born Siegen, 1577; died Antwerp, 1640.

10 Design for the title-page of a history of the Church.
Pencil, pen and brush with brown ink on a prepared ground, heightened with white, 245 × 212 mm.
Inv. no. 0.25
Provenance J. Danser Nijman, sale 19 March 1798, p. 55 (without author's name, but

following two items by A. Diepenbeeck), bought for fl. 14.– by Hendriks for the Teyler Foundation.
Bibliography Scholten, pp. 68–9, 0.25 (as P. P. Rubens); compare C. G. Voorhelm Schneevoogt, *Catalogue des Estampes Gravées d'après P. P. Rubens*, Haarlem, 1873, p. 198, no. 35; M. Rooses, *l'Oeuvre de P. P. Rubens*, Vol. 5, 1892, p. 107; Hollstein, Vol. 4, p. 216, no. 15.

The design, engraved by J. B. Collaert II as after Rubens's invention, is the title page of *De Kerckelijke Historie van de gheboorte Onses Heeren Jesu Christie tot het tegenwoordigh jaer: MDCXXII door F. Dionysium Mudzaert*. This is why Scholten considered the drawing the original design by Rubens. L. Burchard was the first to suggest that Erasmus Quellinus may have worked it out after a slight sketch from Rubens's own hand. Though the style agrees with that of Erasmus Quellinus, he was only fifteen years old in 1622. The technique comes very near to that of a 'Presentation in the Temple' in the Louvre (Lugt, *Flemish Drawings*, Vol. 2, 1189), though the present drawing seems to be in closer connection with Rubens's own imagination. We do not exclude the possibility that, after all, Rubens made the drawing himself, and that the doubt has arisen from the fact, that the technique, chosen as appropriate to the small scale, is unusual in his designs for title pages.

Follower of Sir Peter Paul Rubens

11 Portrait of a middle-aged man (head and shoulders) with a curtain behind him. Black and red chalk, washed with black ink

Follower of Sir Peter Paul Rubens

Hendrick Avercamp

and heightened with white, oval 226 ×
171 mm.
Inv. no. O.26
Provenance ? Jacob de Wit, sale, 10 March
1755; C. Ploos van Amstel (Lugt 2034, 3002
and 3003), sale 3 March 1800, Q.5, sold for
fl. 81.– to Hendriks for the Teyler Foundation
(as by P. P. Rubens).
Bibliography Scholten, p. 69, O.26 (as by
P. P. Rubens); Buisman, p. 5, plate 6 (as by
P. P. Rubens).

This drawing is a free repetition, in subject as
in technique, of an impressive portrait of a man
in the Munich print room (inventory no. 1888)
for which the authorship of Rubens has been
changed hypothetically and not yet entirely
convincingly to that of Jan Cossiers, a pupil
of Rubens, well known for several drawn and
annotated portraits of his children, executed
in a similar technique, though lacking the
strong dark wash. The Munich drawing is
reminiscent of van Dyck's copy after
Bugiardini's portrait of Michelangelo at
Chatsworth (reproduced in M. Jaffé, *Van
Dyck's Antwerp Sketchbook*, Vol. 1, London,
1966, fig. CXLVIII), as well as of van Dyck's
early self-portrait in the Albertina, Vienna
(reproduced *ibid.*, frontispiece, and discussed
pp. 113–14, note 129).

For a considerable time the relation
between the Munich and the Haarlem
drawings has been a matter of controversy,
and the Haarlem sheet also got the hypo-
thetical name of Cossiers. Having discovered
more and more additions in Jakob de Wit's
hand to well known Rubens drawings, the
present writer is now inclined to think that
the Haarlem drawing is entirely by Jakob
de Wit (compare nos. 60–2 of the present
catalogue), who formed his style mainly

during his stay at Antwerp (1709–15).
Whatever the truth of the matter may be, the
drawing is more brilliantly executed than
most copies and may be of interest to those
who are curious to disentangle de Wit's share
in the Rubens legacy. The Munich sheet may
have been retouched by Jacob de Wit also;
and we do not exclude entirely the possibility
that both were copies made by him after a
lost original. The sale catalogue of de Wit's
own collection, dated 10 March 1755,
mentions among other items: 'F.29: two
portraits by van Dyck worked over by de
Wit, and F.32: two heads after Rubens by
J. de Wit.'

Hendrick Avercamp

Painter. Born Amsterdam, 1585; died
Kampen, 1634.

12 A frozen river with skaters, a sledge and
golf players. Signed with the monogram
H A on a log in the foreground. Underneath
on the left an effaced and illegible inscription.
Inscribed by a later hand on the verso
63 geboden.
Watercolour, 175 × 302 mm.
Inv. no. O*7
Provenance C. Ploos van Amstel (Lugt 2034
and 3004), sale 3 March 1800, Amsterdam,
E.7, sold for fl. 200.– to J. Bernard; J. Bernard,
sale 24 November 1834, IJ.2, sold for fl. 1.15
to Gruyter; W. Gruyter Jr.; not in his sale
24 October 1882.
Exhibitions Brussels, 1937–38, no. 44, plate 30.
Bibliography Scholten, p. 92, O*7; C. J.
Welcker, *Hendrick Avercamp*, Zwolle, 1933,
pp. 244–45, T.45 (identical with T.355).
Reproduced in annual edition of *Vereeniging*

Hendrick Avercamp

Esaias van de Velde

tot bevordering van beeldende kunsten, 1925;
N. S. Trivas in the *Connoisseur*, Vol. 103,
London, 1939, pp. 212 and 214, plate 11.

Several of the figures belong to Avercamp's
known repertory. The drawing seems to
originate from the artist's middle period, i.e.
between 1620 and 1625 approximately.
On the verso A standing young man, in a tall
hat, in pencil.

13 The duck catcher, looking out over a
frozen river, with a town in the distance.
Signed with the monogram *H A*.
Black chalk, pen and watercolour, 157 ×
243 mm.
Inv. no. o*3
Provenance S. Fokke, sale 6 December 1784,
N.375, sold for fl. 1.1 with no. 376; W. van
Wessem, sale 6 April 1789, E.38, bought by
IJver for fl. 6.–.
Bibliography Scholten, p. 90, o*3; C. J.
Welcker, *Hendrick Avercamp*, Zwolle, 1933,
p. 244, T.41* (identical with p. 263, T.298, and
with p. 264, T.316), plate 41.

Though the two main buildings in the town
in the distance could each for itself be
identified with a building in Kampen, their
relation to each other is not as shown in the
drawing. The surprisingly broad handling
and the masterful suggestion of the atmosphere of a winter's day permit us to date the
sheet in Avercamp's last period, viz. about
1630–34.

Esaias van de Velde

Etcher and painter. Born Amsterdam,
c. 1590; died at The Hague, 1630.

**14 The coffin containing the body of
Gerrit van Leedenbergh hung on the
gallows,** 15 May 1619. Signed and dated
E. v. Velde. 1619. On the verso are old
inscriptions describing the event.
Black chalk, pen and brown wash, 152 ×
307 mm.
Inv. no. o*11
Provenance J. van der Marck Aegidz, sale
29 November 1773, p. 169, no. 801, sold for
fl. 30.– to Oets; C. Ploos van Amstel, sale
3 March 1800, G.G.G.17, sold for fl. 3.10 to
Versteegh; D. Versteegh, sale 3 November
1823, probably contained in portfolio 4L, sold
to various buyers.
Bibliography E. Michel in *Gazette des Beaux-
Arts*, 2nd series, Vol. 37, 1888, p. 188 (with
reproduction); Scholten, pp. 94–5, o*11.

At the end of August 1618 his conflict as a
Calvinist with the Remonstrant party had
induced Prince Maurice of Orange to arrest
Johan van Oldenbarneveldt, Hugo Grotius,
J. Hoogerbeets and Gerrit van Leedenbergh.
The tragedy was to end by a sentence of
death on Oldenbarneveldt and imprisonment
for Hoogerbeets and Grotius, from which the
latter managed to escape. Leedenbergh,
however, perhaps fearing torture and
certainly sequestration of his goods, committed
suicide before the trial in his Hague prison
during the night of 28–9 September. His
body was not allowed to be interred, and
after van Oldenbarneveldt had been sentenced
and executed, it was condemned to be hung
on a half gallows near The Hague. Esaias van
de Velde must have been present when this
happened. There exists a print published by
Cl. Jsz. Visscher showing the same scene; but
the figures etc. are differently arranged
(Fd. Muller, *Nederlandsche Historieplaten,*

Esaias van de Velde

Jan van Goyen

Pieter Jansz. Saenredam

Amsterdam, 1863, Vol. I, 1400). It seems, however, to be based on this drawing, since the gallows and other instruments of punishment occupy a similar position in both print and drawing.

Jan van Goyen

Painter. Born Leyden, 1596; died at The Hague, 1656.

15 A Dutch river landscape with houses and a bulwark on the left bank. Signed with the monogram *V.G.* and dated *1649*.
Black chalk washed in grey, 159 × 270 mm.
Inv. no. 0.42
Bibliography Scholten, p. 24, 0.42; Buisman, p. 5, no. 8, plate 8.

Situations like the one shown here occurred in several towns in which the fortifications were not entirely consistent, in some places allowing an outlet for traffic by boat, especially at the head of the canals opening into the city's moat. Van Goyen knew such spots in Haarlem and Leyden. The drawing may have been composed from a sketch from nature.

16 Market near a harbour in a Dutch town. Signed with the monogram *J V G* and dated *1653*. One of a pair.
Black chalk and grey wash, 169 × 269 mm.
Inv. no. 0.44
Provenance J. Tak, Haarlem, sale 10 October 1780, no. 43, sold with the pendant no. 44 (Scholten, 0.45) for fl. 32.– to van de Vinne for the Teyler Foundation.
Bibliography Scholten, p. 75, 0.44; Buisman, pp. 5–6, no. 9, plate 9.

With its companion piece, a winter scene of exactly the same size, this drawing belongs to the first acquisitions made for the Foundation after the death of Pieter Teyler (1778) by the Museum's first keeper, Vincent Jansz. van der Vinne. Not only does it prove that drawing pendants was a regular custom in the seventeenth century – hitherto not observed in van Goyen as a draughtsman – but it also explains why commissions for landscape drawings in pairs were often given by the Foundation to artists during the first decades of its existence (compare nos. 60 and 62). The idea may have come from this very acquisition. These landscapes were, of course, invented ones, built up with the aid of notes in sketchbooks used by van Goyen during his travels.

Pieter Jansz. Saenredam

Painter. Born Assendelft, 1597; died Haarlem, 1665.

17 The Château of the king of Bohemia and the Church of St. Cunera at Rhenen.
Annotated by the artist *Pieter Saenredam dese gemaeckt den 27 ende 28 Junij int Jaer 1641*. The foreground may have been completed by I. de Moucheron (1670–1744).
Pen and watercolour, 354 × 464 mm.
Inv. no. 0.81
Provenance ? C. P loos van Amstel, sale 3 March 1800, s.24, sold for fl. 60.– to Roos; ?W. Baartz sale, 6–8 June 1860, no. 323, sold for fl. 5.– to Lamme; Dr C. Hofstede de Groot, sold Amsterdam, 19 January 1904, no. 326, bought in for fl. 1250.–, afterwards bought for fl. 1000.– for the Teyler Foundation.
Exhibitions The Hague, Hofstede de Groot

Pieter Jansz. Saenredam

Roeland Roghman

Collection, 1902, no. 139; Saenredam, Rotterdam, 1937, no. 57, plate 17; Saenredam, Amsterdam, 1938, no. 57, plate 17; Utrecht, 1953, no. 144; Saenredam, Utrecht, 1961, no. 104, plate 104. (Since the Saenredam exhibition of 1937 the wrong provenance has been cited; in the 1961 exhibition those of 104 and 105 have been interchanged.)
Bibliography Not in Scholten; P. T. A. Swillens, *P. J. Saenredam*, Amsterdam, 1935, p. 35, no. 161, plate 119; complete literature in catalogue of Saenredam exhibition, Utrecht, 1961, pp. 155–58.

The church and its tower belong to the best late Gothic architecture in the Netherlands. The 'Koningshuis' was built for Frederick of Bohemia ('the Winter King') in 1630–31 on the order of the States of Utrecht. It was pulled down in 1812. Pieter Saenredam stayed at Rhenen during the summer months of 1644. The foreground scenery, being differently handled, is here hypothetically attributed to Isaac de Moucheron on the analogy of a similar view in the Amsterdam Print Room, where the addition is more clearly marked, and recorded in an inscription.

Roeland Roghman

Painter and etcher. Born Amsterdam, 1597; died there, 1686.

18 Bird's eye view of the house of Moerkerken, drawn from the spire of the village church. Signed and dated *R R 1647* (partly cut off). Annotated by the artist on the verso '*het huys te Moerkerken van booven van de kerck geteekent*'.

Black chalk and grey wash, 340 × 495 mm.
Inv. no. O**32
Provenance Possibly Laurens Baeck; Albert (or Hillebrand) Bentes (died 1708) (MS. inventory kept in Print Room, Amsterdam, no. 100); Christiaen van Hoeck; Anthonie van Hoeck; C. Ploos van Amstel, sale 3 March 1800, among KK.3, bought by Roos (KK.1–7, fl. 2000.– for 248 drawings); J. Cats and S. Goblé, 16 April 1800, B.79 for fl. 2.– to Roos; (anonymous) sale Amsterdam, 16 December 1805, E.6; J. H. Molkenboer, sale 17 October 1825, p. 20, sold for fl.5.– to de Vries; Mlle Roelofs, sale 2 April 1873, no. 84, sold with two others for fl. 51.– to Gruyter for the Teyler Foundation.
Exhibitions Brussels, 1961, p. 103, no. 102, with literature.
Bibliography Scholten, p. 120, O**32; 'Register van Adelijke Huysen, Kastelen, etc. gelegen in Holland, Uitregt, Gelderland, etc. alle getekent door Roeland Roghman meest in de jaren 1646 en 1647', MS. inventory preserved in the Print Room, Amsterdam, under no. 100. A second drawing, representing the house seen from behind, from the Jhr. W. Six collection passed to Dr C. Hofstede de Groot and then to Jhr. W. A. Beelaerts van Blokland (no. 101 in the Bentes MS.). A third drawing is listed under no. 20 in the Bentes MS.

The old 'Court of Moerkerken' and the village of the same name were situated in the 'Hoeksche Waard' near the old Meuse, on land which had been reclaimed after being inundated by the disastrous flood of Saint Elizabeth's day, 1421. The house, once occupied by a noble family, can be distinguished in the distance by its twin-gabled front. It was surrounded by gardens and orchards. There are only a few instances of

Roeland Roghman

Sir Anthony van Dyck

Roghman climbing a church tower to get a bird's eye view of a castle he wished to sketch. The custom had begun to spread about these years, and we know that Jan van Goyen drew the country around Haarlem on all sides from a platform in the spire above the crossing of St. Bavo some years previously, in 1644. These early attempts were to be followed by the famous views of Haarlem from the top of a high dune by Jacob van Ruysdael.

19 The castle of Culemborgh
Inscribed on the verso in ink *Cuylenburgh*.
Black chalk and grey wash, 332 × 452 mm.
Inv. no. O**42
Provenance Possibly Laurens Baeck; Albert (or Hillebrand) Bentes (MS. inventory in Print Room, Amsterdam, no. 65); Christiaen van Hoeck; Anthonie van Hoeck; C. Ploos van Amstel, sale 3 March 1800, among KK.II 55 and 56, bought by Roos (KK.1–7, consisting of 248 drawings for fl. 2000.–); sale J. Cats and S. Goblé, 16 April 1800, B.68 or 69), together for fl. 18.–, bought by Roos; Abr. de Haas, sale 8 November 1824, U.32, bought for fl. 7.5 by Bernard; J. Bernard, sale 24 November 1834, U.10, bought for fl. 8.5 by Gruyter; W. Gruyter, sale 24–25 October 1882, no. 219, bought for fl. 64.40 for the Teyler Foundation.
Bibliography Scholten, p. 122, O**42; Bentes Register, no. 42; the MS. inventory of 248 items belonging to Mr Bentes mentions two views of Culemborgh Castle (no. 65).

The castle was built about the middle of the fourteenth century by Johan, Heer van Culemborgh, to replace an older one. The high tower and the great hall adjoining it, both visible, belonged to his building works, to which others were added afterwards. The occupations by Spanish troops in the sixteenth century and by the French in 1672 and 1673 were among the causes of its decay, and in 1735 the stones obtained from pulling it down were used to reinforce a dike of the Zuiderzee. Today nothing remains of it.

Sir Anthony van Dyck

Painter and etcher. Born Antwerp, 1599; died London, 1641.

20 The Entombment of Christ.
Black chalk, pen and brush with dark brown ink and watercolour on buff paper, 220 × 185 mm.
Inv. no. O*15
Exhibitions van Dyck, Antwerp, 1949, no. 83; van Dyck, Antwerp-Rotterdam, 1960, no. 5.
Bibliography Scholten, p. 96, O*15; and complete survey in H. Vey, *Die Zeichnungen Anton van Dijcks*, 1962, pp. 77–8, no. 6, figs. 8–9.

A copy of the recto exists in the British Museum (Hind, *Dutch and Flemish Catalogue*, Vol. 2, no. 9). Vey considers the colours in the Teyler drawing as perhaps added by another hand, but the pen lines seem to cover them. Moreover the same blue and red occur in another original drawing of the same subject at Chatsworth (Vey, *op. cit.*, no. 4; reproduced in colours, though not very faithfully, in *Great Drawings of all times*, New York, 1962, Vol. 2, no. 543). Other versions are recorded, though now lost. As far as is known, no painting resulted from these early sketches by van Dyck. They show few signs of dependence on Rubens, anyhow as far as the composition is concerned. The seed of the Haarlem drawing may be sought in a transcription after Rubens in van Dyck's Antwerp sketch-

Rembrandt van Rijn

Jan Lievens

406 look out on low house fronts and what seems to be a mill rising up above them. The better identification of this spot may shed more light on the question.

A later copy of the present drawing mentioning the subject as 'his Child's Nurse' in eighteenth century handwriting, was in the collection of Mr A. Brod, London, in 1967, and proves again that the traditional title existed already at that time.

25 Christ carrying the Cross, with St. Veronica wiping His forehead.
Pen and brown wash heightened with white on a sheet of paper consisting of two parts, 174 × 273 mm.
Inv. no. O*62a
Provenance Count M. von Fries (Lugt 2903); M. Marignane (Lugt 1872); bought for the Teyler Foundation through Dr C. Hofstede de Groot in 1920.
Exhibitions Amsterdam, 1932, no. 312; Haarlem, 1951, no. 175; Amsterdam, 1956, no. 202; Amsterdam, 1964–65, Rijksmuseum, 'Bijbelsche inspiratie', no. 110.
Bibliography Not in Scholten; Benesch, Vol. 5, p. 269, no. 923, fig. 1134 (with bibliography); *Great Drawings of all times*, Vol. 2, New York, 1962, no. 596.

We agree with Benesch in dating this drawing about 1653. The hands of the figure on the left raising both his arms are reminiscent of those of Christ in 'La Petite Tombe' of 1652 (Hind, *Rembrandt*, 256), and they are in the direction of the etching, which points to a date after that had been printed. During the next years Rembrandt was to occupy himself intensely with what became his profoundest interpretations of Christ's Passion.

Jan Lievens

Painter and etcher. Born Leyden, 1607; died Amsterdam, 1674.

26 Portrait of doctor Frans de le Boe Sylvius. Signed with monogram *I. L.* and dated *1657.*
Black chalk, 419 × 308 mm.
Inv. no. P.6
Provenance ? C. Ploos van Amstel, as a portrait of Constantijn Huyghens, sale 3 March 1800, c.16; sold for fl. 9.10 to Josi; probably J. de Bosch, sale 5 October 1767, no. 254; sale de la Sablonière and Ekama, Amsterdam, 30 June 1891; sold for fl. 195.– to the Teyler Foundation.
Exhibitions London, 1929, no. 647.
Bibliography Scholten, p. 129, P.6; Reproduced in Kleinmann's Series; H. Schneider, *Jan Lievens*, Haarlem, 1932, p. 207, z.110; E. D. Baumann, *François de le Boe Sylvius*, 1949, *passim.*

In 1657 Lievens was living at The Hague, and it is conceivable that the son of the better known poet Constantijn Huyghens, Constantijn II, then 35 years of age, is the subject of the portrait. However, there are two copies of the drawing, and the one in the British Museum (Hind, *Dutch and Flemish Catalogue*, Vol. 1, no. 29) gives Sylvius as the sitter. That is probably the more reliable identification, as the name Huyghens may have been wrongly given to the portrait since Ploos van Amstel owned it. Franciscus de le Boe Sylvius (1614–72), doctor of medicine and professor at Leyden, is well known for several important discoveries in the anatomy of the brain and other parts of the body, and in the part played by chemical processes in physiology;

above all he discovered the tubercles of the lungs, whereby he established the cause of tuberculosis. His courses at Leyden were attended by more students than those of any other doctor until the time of Boerhave.

The portrait is an example of a finished drawing made for its own sake, and not as a study for a picture.

Jan Asselijn

Painter. Born Dieppe, 1610; died Amsterdam, 1652.

27 The inside of the Arch of Titus, Rome, with the relief representing the Emperor on his triumphal chariot. Inscribed on the verso in chalk *N° 16*.
Black chalk, strengthened with pen and brown ink, and brush and black ink, 268 × 189 mm..
Inv. no. P.94
Bibliography Scholten, p. 155, P.94.

The arch was erected under the Emperor Domitian (A.D. 81?) to commemorate his father Vespasian and his brother Titus and the capture of Jerusalem (A.D. 70). At the time Asselijn drew it, it had lost its side walls, but the original reliefs of extraordinarily good workmanship still exist today, though in a mutilated state. Both the one represented and its opposite showing the treasures of the temple being carried in the procession, were a favourite motif of Dutch artists in Rome. Asselijn executed his between 1632 and 1637, following an example set by C. van Poelenburgh in a drawing of 1621 in the Print Room at Amsterdam (reproduced in I. Q. van Regteren Altena, *Vereeuwigde Stad,*

Amsterdam, 1964, plate 27), but Asselijn dwelt more on the quality of the homogeneous lump of chiselled and worn marble, and the effect of the sunlight falling on it.

Adriaen van Ostade

Painter. Born Haarlem, 1610; died there, 1685.

28 A couple of peasants dancing to the music of a fiddler in a barn. Signed and dated *A V ostaden 1636*.
Black chalk, pen and brush with brown ink, 206 × 161 mm.
Inv. no. P.74
Provenance C. M. van Gogh; sold to Scheltema in 1890; he sold it to W. P. Knowles (Lugt 2643), sale 25–26 June 1895, no. 474, bought for fl. 158.– by the Teyler Foundation.
Bibliography Scholten, p. 148, P.74 (as Adriaen van Ostade); Reproduced in Kleinmann's Series, Vol. 1, no. 59; *Great Drawings of all times*, Vol. 2, New York, 1962, no. 605.

This is an excellent sample of the early manner of Adriaen van Ostade, which betrays the influence of Rembrandt's *clair-obscur*. The signature has been added afterwards, but we think in the same year, partly on account of the date which fits exactly, partly because of the unusual form of the signature: *Ostaden*, which is found only on paintings of that period. We do not see any reason to attribute it to Izaäck van Ostade.

Anthonie Waterloo

Painter and etcher. Born Lille, 1609/10; died Utrecht, 1676 or afterwards.

Anthonie Waterloo

Govaert Flinck

29 View of Nijmegen with the Valkhof
on the left in the foreground. On the verso the
(unexplained) inscription *J d L 6* in red chalk.
Black chalk, washed in black ink, 402 ×
517 mm. One of a pair.
Inv. no. u★17
Provenance Jhr. J. Goll van Franckenstein
(Lugt 2987), sale 1 July 1833, т.27, bought for
fl. 21.– by Rombouts, who also acquired
u.15, the companion piece, for fl. 21.–, thus
preventing them from being separated;
L. Dupper, sale 28 June 1870, no. 426, acquired
for fl. 29.– for the Teyler Foundation, which
bought also u.427, the companion view for
fl. 24.–.
Bibliography Scholten, p. 399, u★17; K. Plath,
Het Valkhof te Nijmegen, Amsterdam, 1898,
pp. 67–9, 104–06; P. Leendertz, *Het Valkhof
te Nijmegen* (publication of 'Gelre'), Arnhem,
1930, p. 1, no. 3 and *passim*.

Nijmegen is seen while its stronghold is still
intact, and the castle Valkhof, once used by
Charlemagne as a hunting residence and
enlarged by successive German Emperors,
shows parts of its inner and outer wall with a
road between both on the bank of the river
Waal. The summit is crowned by the 'giant
tower' which, when demolished in 1795, was
estimated to provide almost eleven thousand
tons of rubble (tons measuring 6 cubic
Amsterdam feet, i.e. about 2 cubic metres).
In fact the year 1795 witnessed the removal of
a secular architectural complex which had
been immortalized in some of van Goyen's
most impressive paintings. The central tower
is surrounded by the different buildings of the
once imperial palace, during Waterloo's time
in use by the government of Gelderland. In the
town itself the late medieval church of St.

Stephen can be distinguished in its elevated
position.
Waterloo was one of the first artists to draw
views of several Dutch towns situated along
the popular route Amsterdam–Utrecht–
Arnhem–Nijmegen. He also travelled to
Hamburg and as far as Danzig. At Nijmegen
he executed a series of large views of the
Valkhof seen from different angles from the
outside, as well as its inner court. They are
now kept in the Teyler Museum (two sheets),
the Archives of Nijmegen, the Museum of
Groningen, the Print Room at Amsterdam
and the British Museum. The view dated
1670 in the F. Lugt collection, Paris, shows a
different treatment, and we consider those
mentioned to have been done at an earlier
date.

Govaert Flinck

Painter. Born Cleves, 1615; died Amsterdam,
1660.

30 Study of a boy seated on a low support.
Signed *G. flinck.*
Black and white chalk on dull blue paper,
299 × 234 mm.
Inv. no. p★7
Provenance A. van der Willigen, sale 11 June
1874, no. 90, sold for fl. 30.– to Dirksen;
bought June 1884 by Knowles; A. P. Knowles,
sale 25–6 June 1885, no. 234, sold for fl. 22.–
to the Teyler Foundation.
Exhibitions 'Rembrandt als Leermeester',
Leyden, 1956, no. 122.
Bibliography H. Havard, *l'Art et les artistes
hollandais*, Vol. 2, p. 174; Scholten, p. 160,
p★7; Buisman, p. 7, plate 22; J. H. J. Mellaart,
Dutch drawings of the XVIIth century, London,

1926, p. 28, plate 12; J. W. von Moltke, *Govaert Flinck*, Amsterdam, 1965, pp. 53, 196, DII7, plate 64.

The pose is not found in any figure in Flinck's paintings. The costume with tassels hanging from broad breeches points to a date in the fifties at the earliest.

Ferdinand Bol

Painter and etcher. Born Dordrecht, 1616; died Amsterdam, 1680.

31 Abraham kneeling in prayer beside the prepared sacrificial dish.
Black chalk and brush with black and brown ink on cream paper, 290 × 220 mm.
Inv. no. P*8
Provenance Jacob de Vos, sale 30 October 1833, no. 6, sold for fl. 65.- to Hulswit (not in his sale 1822); Mr H. van Cranenburgh, sale 26 October 1858, no. 246, bought by Buffa for the Teyler Foundation for fl. 15.-.
Bibliography Scholten, p. 160, P*8; Buisman, p. 7, plate 23; Bernt, Vol. 1, no. 90; W. R. Valentiner, *Rembrandts Handzeichnungen*, Vol. 1, Stuttgart-Berlin-Leipzig, 1925, p. XXV.

The novel feature in Bol's subject is that he separated the figure of Abraham from the scene of the Sacrifice of Isaac, which is clearly meant (rather than Gideon, as in Judges VI, 21), witness the sacrificial implements in the foreground and the knife in his belt. A prayer by Abraham is not mentioned in the text of Genesis, so this is one of the two occasions on which the Angel speaks to Abraham (Genesis XXII, 11–2 and 15–8). Bol must have

known Rembrandt's early painted version of the Sacrifice and treated it similarly in painting. This time, however, he limited himself to the one figure in prayer as represented, for example, by Rembrandt in a drawing in the Print Room, Amsterdam (Benesch 59), considered a study for the etching of 1632 showing St. Jerome in prayer (Hind, *Rembrandt*, 94). At all events Bol achieved an impressive effect by laying the whole emphasis on Abraham's agony and setting the scene against an appropriately dark background.

Thomas Wijck

Painter. Born Beverwijk, *c.* 1616; died Haarlem 1679.

32 A court-yard in a Roman house.
Signed *T Wijck f* (the initials united).
Black chalk and grey wash, 154 × 232 mm.
Inv. no. P*11
Provenance Jhr. J. Goll van Franckenstein (Lugt 2987), sale 1 July 1833, L.10, bought for fl. 15.10 by Michaelis for the Teyler Foundation.
Bibliography Scholten, p. 161, P*11.

Another drawing of the same subject, but with different figures and touched with the pen, exists in the Fodor collection, Amsterdam (catalogue 1863, no. 273). It might be the earlier version. The subject is a popular one with Thomas Wijck, who drew various similar *cortiles* while staying at Rome before 1642. He may have continued to do so when he returned to Holland, and the handling of the present drawing seems to point, in fact, to a later date.

Gerard Terborch

Philips de Koninck

Gerard Terborch

Painter. Born Zwolle, 1617; died Deventer, 1681.

33 The vegetable-market before the town hall in Haarlem. Traces of a cut-off signature in the lower right margin.
Black chalk, pen and grey wash, 185 × 275 mm.
Inv. no. P*19
Provenance C. Ploos van Amstel (Lugt 3002 and 3004, mentioning a wrong year 1641), sale 3 March 1800, x.4, sold with x.3 for fl. 10.– to Fokke (not in his sale 1784); H. de Kat, sale 4 March 1867, no. 251, bought for fl. 5.50 by Vis Blokhuizen; D. Vis Blokhuizen, probably second sale 23 October 1871, no. 575; compare also last sale 29 April 1872, no. 385, bought for fl. 1.– by van Gogh; van Reede van Oudshoorn, sale 28 October 1874, no. 217 sold as by Gezina Terborch for fl. 87.– to the Teyler Foundation.
Bibliography Scholten, p. 164, P*19; J. H. J. Mellaart, *Dutch Drawings of the seventeenth century*, London, 1926, p. 36, plate 71; I. Q. van Regteren Altena, *Dutch Master Drawings*, London, 1949, pp. XVI–XVII, no. 13, plate 13; J. G. van Gelder, *Prenten en Tekeningen*, Amsterdam, 1958, pp. 27, 94, plate 54; S. J. Gudlaugsson, *Geraert Ter Borgh*, Vol. 1, The Hague, 1959, pp. 26–7 (with reproduction).

Sketched during the years of the artist's apprenticeship with Pieter Molijn (1633–35) at Haarlem, the year 1641 having probably been incorrectly substituted for 1634 by Ploos van Amstel. The town hall shows its oldest part, the old hall of the Counts of Holland, and the Renaissance additions plus the tower and the scaffold built into the market place. There exists an affinity in subject matter with the prints of Jan van de Velde, but Terborch was a more delicate observer.

Philips de Koninck

Painter. Born Amsterdam, 1619; died there, 1688.

34 View of a river with farmers reaping corn in a field.
Pen and brush with brown ink and watercolour, 145 × 200 mm.
Inv. no. P*28
Provenance J. H. Molkenboer, sale 7 October 1825, A.7, sold for fl. (1)350.– to Hulswit; H. van Cranenburgh, sale 26 October 1858, G.155, sold for fl. 1200.– to de Vries for de Vos; J. de Vos jr. (Lugt 1450), sale 22 May 1883, sold for fl. 705.– to de Vries for the Teyler Foundation.
Bibliography Scholten, p. 167, P*28; J. H. J. Mellaart, *Dutch Drawings*, London, 1926, p. 28, plate 15; H. Gerson, *Philips Koninck*, Berlin, 1936, pp. 66, 142, z.38 and plate 39.

According to Gerson the drawing belongs to the artist's late period, when several of his drawings come near to those of Lambert Doomer and of Koninck's brother-in-law Jacob Furnerius. Though Gerson calls it a landscape in Gelderland, we doubt whether it represents an actual spot. It is more likely that reminiscences of the Rhine near Arnhem have been fused into an imaginary scene.

Claes Pietersz. Berchem

Painter and etcher. Born Haarlem, 1620;
died Amsterdam, 1683.

35 A seated shepherd in a sheepskin coat
and a broad hat, seen from the back.
Oily black chalk on buff paper, 319 ×
215 mm.
Inv. no. Q.9
Exhibitions Washington, etc., 1958–59,
no. 92.
Bibliography Scholten, p. 186, Q.9; reproduced
in Kleinmann's Series I, plate 28; Ilse von
Sick, *Nicolaes Berchem*, Berlin, 1930, pp. 34
and 63, no. 253 (wrongly described as
heightened with white); I. Q. van Regteren
Altena, *Vereeuwigde Stad*, Amsterdam, 1964,
p. 96, no. 7, plate 7.

A study from life of a shepherd in the Roman
Campagna, probably made during Berchem's
second stay in Rome from 1653 till 1655, since
when such figures, usually seated on a
donkey, often occur in his paintings, etchings
and drawn compositions. It is a unique
achievement of Berchem's craft to render the
material quality of an animal's skin as vividly
as he does here.

**36 Shepherds resting near the ruins of
Castle Brederode.**
Black chalk, pen and wash and light brown
ink, 457 × 585 mm.
Inv. no. U*12
Provenance Probably Jer. Tonneman, sale 21
October 1754, C.I, sold for fl. 245.– to de
Leth; probably W. P. Kops, sale 14 March
1808, H.I, sold for fl. 290.– to van Leen;
O. Vis Blokhuysen, Rotterdam, sale 23
October 1871, no. 52; van Reede van
Oudtshoorn, sale 28 October 1874, sold for
fl. 40.– to the Teyler Foundation.
Bibliography Scholten, pp. 397–98, U*12;
Ilse von Sick, *Nicolaes Berchem*, Berlin, 1930,
p. 61, no. 202 (in both as an unidentified
landscape).

This is one of Berchem's few exceptionally
large landscapes, in which he takes pleasure in
displaying all his skill and virtuosity. The
subject can be identified as the ruins of the
large castle of the Brederodes, parts of which
still stand at the foot of the dunes north of
Haarlem; it was described as such in the
catalogue of the auction of the Kops collection
(1808). The view is taken from the ruins of
the south-western tower, fancifully called the
'Tethburg tower' in the romantic age,
looking towards the still existent body of the
north-western tower. The composition seems
to be based on sketches made on the spot.
The drawing dates from the artist's later
years.
   The Heeren van Brederode descended from
the House of Teylingen, which was related to
that of the Counts of Holland, and they ruled
over large parts of Holland. The castle was
built in the thirteenth century but it was so
worn by calamities that it was already an
uninhabited ruin when Berchem visited it.

Albert Cuyp

Painter. Born Dordrecht, 1620; died there,
1691.
37 View of the town of Rhenen taken
from the north.
Black chalk and watercolour, 190 ×
307 mm.
Inv. no. P*42

Albert Cuyp

Constantyn Huyghens

Provenance van der Willigen, sale 10 June 1874, no. 68, bought for fl. 825.– for the Teyler Foundation.
Bibliography Scholten, p. 172, P*42; Buisman, p. 8, no. 28, plate 28.

The town of Rhenen, with its beautiful spire rising above the hills along the Rhine, was a favourite sketching-ground for artists in the seventeenth century. Hercules Seghers initiated such exercises. This sheet seems to date from an early period in Cuyp's career (*c.* 1645). A second view of the same scene, very similar in all respects, the foreground excepted, is in the Berlin Print Room (Inv. 1170, reproduced in E. Bock-J. Rosenberg, *Die Niederländischen Meister*, Berlin, 1930, plate 83). The present drawing gives the impression of being the earlier one, probably done on the spot, whereas the herdsmen and the flock on the Berlin sheet and its more formal treatment suggest that it is a more studied and embellished repetition. Both, however, must date from the same time.

38 Cattle at rest on the bank of a large river with part of a town in the distance.
Black chalk washed with brownish ink on buff paper, 208 × 452 mm.
Inv. no. P*40
Provenance P. Blussé van Zuidland en Velgersdijk, sale 15 March 1870, no. 54, sold for fl. 153.– to Gruyter for the Teyler Foundation.
Exhibitions Brussels, 1961, no. 104, plate 33.
Bibliography E. Michel, in *Gazette des Beaux-Arts*, 4th series, Vol. 7, 1892, reproduced p. 237; Scholten, p. 171, P*40; reproduced in Kleinmann's Series; Bernt, Vol. 1, no. 164; J. G. van Gelder, *Prenten en Tekeningen*, Amsterdam, 1958, pp. 37, 96, plate 100.

The river would suggest the Meuse, the view being taken from opposite Dordrecht. But the walls of the town and the gate seen behind them, instead of representing the Groothoofdspoort, as one would expect, occur again in the large view of a town supposed to be Flushing (sold with the H. Oppenheimer collection and reproduced in the sale catalogue of 10–4 July 1936, no. 226). Cuyp may have used the same buildings twice for the sake of his composition. Though one of his major drawings, the composition of the Teyler sheet, as far as we know, cannot be recognised in any of the large canvasses known from Cuyp's hand. The drawing may date from the sixties.

Constantyn Huyghens

Secretary to William III, diarist and dilettante draughtsman. Born at The Hague, 1621; died there, 1697.

39 A view of the Meuse at Smeermaes.
Annotated by the artist *Smeermaes 5 Aug. 1676.*
Pen with light brown ink, 125 × 237 mm.
Inv. no. Q*57
Exhibitions Paris, 1950, no. 134; Washington, etc., 1958–59, p. 43, no. 105.
Bibliography Scholten, p. 232; Q*57; J. H. J. Mellaart, *Dutch Drawings of the seventeenth century*, London, 1926, p. 35, plate 63.

This panoramic view strikingly anticipates modern English landscape etching. The Meuse is seen from the south with the town of Maastricht on the horizon, all its buildings and the Pietersberg being clearly visible. On 1 July 1673, thanks to Vauban's military engineering skill, Maastricht had been captured for Louis XIV, and now, in 1676, William III had laid siege to it. Two black stripes indicate the pontoon bridges connecting the headquarters of William III at Smeermaes with the Dutch encampment visible on the left bank. The barges in the foreground may have been bringing munitions. Among the continuous fierce battles 5 August was a quiet but sad day for Huyghens: he had to look after the dead body of his great-nephew Louis Sweerts (Zuerius), a cavalry captain, killed the previous day, until it could be conveyed on a waggon to 's Hertogenbosch (*Journaal van Constantijn Huyghens, den zoon*, Vol. 1, Utrecht, 1881, p. 125). His diary is silent about the superb and peaceful drawing which he executed in these circumstances during the morning hours. The siege had to be broken up, and only at the Peace of Nijmegen (1678) was the town returned to the Dutch Republic.

Jan de Bray

Painter and engraver. Born Haarlem, *c.* 1627; died there, 1697.

40 Presumed portrait of Dirck de Bray.

Signed and dated *1658 J D Bray* with the initials as a monogram.
Black chalk, 192 × 152 mm.
Inv. no. 0.52ᵃ
Provenance C. Ploos van Amstel (Lugt 3002 and 3004), sale 3 March 1800, probably c.22, sold for fl. 60.– to C. S. Roos; Mr H. van Cranenburgh, sale 26 October 1858, no. 224, sold for fl. 60.– to Gruyter; de la Sablonière and Ekema, sale Amsterdam, 30 June 1891, no. 25, sold for fl. 48.– to Gutekunst;

W. P. Knowles (Lugt 2643), sale 25 June 1895, no. 113, sold for fl. 70.– to Lanz; P. Langerhuizen Lz (Lugt 2095), sale 29 April 1919, no. 99, reproduced plate 7, bought by Trautscholdt for the Teyler Foundation for fl. 650.–.
Bibliography Not mentioned by Scholten; Buisman, p. 9, plate 34; J. W. von Moltke in *Marburger Jahrbuch*, Vol. 11–12, 1938–39, p. 426, note 7; p. 501, z.64; p. 503, plate 70; J. W. von Moltke in *Jaarboekje Haerlem*, 1937, p. 40, note 4; Bernt, Vol. 1, no. 118; H. van Hall, *Portretten van Nederlandse Kunstenaars*, Amsterdam, 1964, p. 43 under Dirck de Bray, sub-paragraph 2.

The inscription by Ploos van Amstel mentions 'the portrait of de Bray, son of Salomon de Bray. Jacob de Bray f. 1658'.

Jan de Bray drew some portraits of members of his family, similar in size and handling. That of his father occurs twice (Berlin, London) and one of his brothers, Joseph (who became a priest), may be recognised in a sheet in the Fodor collection, Amsterdam. There has been much confusion about the portrait now shown. First of all because Ploos van Amstel thought Jacob de Bray was the artist who signed *J. de Bray*. Jacob was his brother, whom we do not know to have been an artist at all. It was perhaps because he recognised the error that Gutekunst cut off an inscription underneath the drawing. Knowles afterwards added a border line to complete the three already existing ones, which framed the portrait. The inscription must have mentioned that the sitter was a son of Salomon de Bray. The other mistake was due to the compilers of the Ploos van Amstel sale catalogue, who gave the impression that the sitter was a son of the J. de Bray, mentioned in the preceding lot.

Jan de Bray

Jacob van Ruysdael

In reality the sitter was one of the artist's brothers, and we are inclined to think that it was Dirck. His etched self-portrait of a later date supports the identification. It is reproduced in F. G. Waller, *Biographisch Woordenboek van Noord-Nederlandsche Graveurs*, The Hague, 1938, plate IX, facing p. 50; and mentioned by H. van Hall, *Portretten van Nederlandsche Beeldende Kunstenaars*, Amsterdam, 1963, p. 43, but only in a note in sub-paragraph 1, instead of occupying a number for itself.

Jacob van Ruysdael

Painter and etcher. Born Haarlem, *c.* 1629; died Amsterdam, 1682.

41 Three old cottages at Bentheim.
Black chalk and grey wash, 148 × 200 mm.
Inv. no. Q*51
Bibliography Scholten, p. 230, Q*51; reproduced in Kleinmann's Series 2, plate 15; Buisman, p. 9, plate 35; J. Rosenberg, *Jacob van Ruisdael*, Berlin, 1928, p. 113, no. 29.

Ruysdael must have seen these houses when sketching at Bentheim, before 1653 (the date on the Beit picture, H.d.G. 25). From the material gathered there he afterwards composed several of his grandest paintings, among others H.d.G. 798, showing a range of similar buildings, H.d.G. 791 and H.d.G. 782, where a road along them leads up to the castle. In the beginning of the nineteenth century Bentheim was still a favourite sketching ground for artists from Amsterdam, as is shown by the similar 'Houses at Bentheim' by A. Brondgeest in a private collection at Amsterdam. The drawing shown here may have been a later reminiscence from Ruysdael's early journey, or a slight sketch from nature worked out at a later date.

42 The ruins of the Castle of Kostverloren
near Amsterdam. Inscribed on the verso *Kostverloren door I VR* (monogram).
Black chalk and grey wash, 203 × 291 mm.
Inv. no. Q*52
Provenance C. Ploos van Amstel (Lugt 3003), sale 3 March 1800, T.10, sold with T.9 for fl. 176.– to Boddens; Baron J. Verstolk van Soelen, sale 22 March 1847, no. 220, sold for fl. 405.– to Roos for Leembruggen; G. Leembruggen, sale 5 March 1866, no. 542, sold for fl. 525.– to Gruyter for the Teyler Foundation.
Bibliography Scholten, p. 231, Q*52; F. Lugt, *Wandelingen met Rembrandt*, Amsterdam, 1915, pp. 108–09, plate 70; not mentioned by J. Rosenberg, *Jacob van Ruysdael*, Berlin, 1928.

The castle was built on the bank of the Amstel about 1500 and received its name when the costs for repair had become disastrous, Kostverloren meaning lost earnings. It burned down in 1650, and what it was before can be seen in Ruysdael drawings at Hamburg and in the F. Lugt collection (see the exhibition catalogue, *Dessins de paysagistes hollandais du XVIIe siècle*, Brussels, Rotterdam, Paris, Bern, 1968–69, no. 126, with extensive comments and bibliography). The present sheet shows it after the fire, as does a picture, bearing Ruysdael's monogram (H.d.G. 101), sold in London, 1 April 1960, no. 73, which is entirely based on our drawing. The authorship of the drawing is thereby fully established and its broad treatment, in this case, cannot be a reason for

Jacob van Ruysdael

Gabriel Metsu

suggesting Meindert Hobbema as an alternative candidate. But there exists a variant of the picture by Hobbema, and one certainly derived from it, though differently lighted (formerly in the Sedelmeyer, Perkins and Borden Collections).

Ruysdael's drawing may have been made during his first years in Amsterdam, i.e. towards 1660.

43 Tombs in the Portuguese Jewish Cemetery at Ouderkerk on the Amstel. Signed *IvRuisdael f* (the initials united). One of a pair, etched in reverse by C. Blootelingh, 1670.
Black chalk washed with black ink, with traces of transfer on to the copperplate; the verso reddened, 190 × 283 mm.
Inv. no. Q*48
Provenance The pair: D. Muilman, sale 29 March 1773, no. 1120, sold for fl. 69.– to de Vos; Jacob de Vos Sr., not in his sale; A. Saportas, sale 14 May 1832, A.3, sold for fl. 410.– (or fl. 465.–) to Hulswit; Mr H. van Cranenburgh, sale 26 October 1858, sold for fl. 905.– to Buffa for the Teyler Foundation.
Exhibitions London, 1929, no. 699; Commemorative Catalogue, 1930, p. 231; Brussels, 1937–38, no. 132, plate 81.
Bibliography Scholten, p. 229, Q*48; reproduced in Kleinmann's Series; J. Rosenberg, *Jakob Ruisdael*, Berlin, 1928, pp. 31, 113, no. 27, plate 59; P. Zwarts in *Oudheidkundig Jaarboek*, Vol. 8, 1928, pp. 232–49; K. E. Simon, *Jacob van Ruisdael*, Berlin, 1930, pp. 31, 68, 84; K. E. Simon in *Festschrift Ad. Goldschmidt*, Berlin, 1935, p. 158; H. F. Wijnman in *Oud Holland*, Vol. 44, 1932, p. 179; I. Q. van Regteren Altena, *Dutch Master Drawings of the Seventeenth Century*, London, 1949, p. XXVI, no. 48; Exhibition

catalogue, Brussels, 1961, pp. 122–23, no. 124 (the companion piece) with extensive literature on the pair.

The tombs are those of important early members and rabbis of the Portuguese Jews settled in Amsterdam, and are still preserved *in situ*. The drawings were engraved afterwards by Abraham Blootelingh (1670) and seem to have been meant to remain as companion drawings for their own sake. However, Ruysdael made use of motives occurring in them in paintings like the one in Detroit and the Dresden one, which inspired Goethe's 'Ruisdael als Dichter', 1816. Another pair of similar subjects, retouched by D. Dalens, is now in the collection of Mrs Kramarsky, New York. Rosenberg seems to date these drawings before 1655 ('Wanderjahre'), which we consider too early. It is not necessary, though, to go so far as to accept the year on the print as the date of the drawings too.

Gabriel Metsu

Painter. Born Leyden (?), *c.* 1627; died Amsterdam, 1667.

44 Seated cavalier raising a glass.
Black and white chalks slightly washed, on brown paper, 227 × 181 mm.
Inv. no. R.35
Provenance Probably Jhr. J. G. Goll van Franckenstein (as G. Metsu), sale 1 June 1833, K.7, bought for fl. 40.– by Roos; Baron J. Verstolk van Soelen (as J. Uchterveld), sale 22 March 1847, no. 183, bought for fl. 112.– by Michaelis for the Teyler Foundation.
Bibliography Scholten, pp. 253–54, R.35 (as Terborch); Buisman, p. 7, no. 24, plate 24,

Gabriel Metsu

Jan Hackaert

Willem van de Velde the Younger

Adriaen van de Velde

(as Terborch); I. Q. van Regteren Altena, *Gabriel Metsu as a draughtsman*, Master Drawings, Vol. 1, 1963, pp. 16, 19, no. 19, plate 12.

The attribution of this drawing was proposed on the strength of stylistic elements. The seated cavalier in his modish attire is exactly what one might expect from Metsu's hand during his later, Amsterdam period.

Jan Hackaert

Painter and etcher. Born Amsterdam, *c.* 1629; died there, after 1685.

45 Alpine landscape with a bridge among steep rocks. Inscribed *Jan Both. 16.*
Pen and brush with light brown ink, 200 × 290 mm.
Inv. no. P.56

Though inscribed *Jan Both*, this drawing so conspicuously shows the hand of Jan Hackaert, that it is best to describe it under his name. We may cite Hackaert's drawings in Leyden (reproduced in J. J. de Gelder, *Honderd Teekeningen . . . in Leiden*, Rotterdam, 1920, plate 95) and in private Swiss possession (reproduced in *Handzeichnungen aus schweizer Privatbesitz*, exhibited Bremen–Zürich, 1967, no. 177) which show foliage treated similarly and the use of oblique parallel hatchings. Since the number 16 after the name is clearly not a date, Hackaert may have re-interpreted in his own style an original drawing by Jan Both, the sixteenth of a series, though fir trees hardly occur in Both's landscapes.

Willem van de Velde the Younger

Painter. Born Leyden, 1633; died Greenwich, 1707.

46 The hull of a three masted man-of-war, seen from the stern.
Black chalk and grey wash on a sheet enlarged on two sides, 396 × 545 mm.
Inv. no. U*26a
Provenance Bought with two similar drawings in 1864 for fl. 45.–.
Bibliography Scholten, p. 402, U*26a. M. S. Robinson, *Van de Velde drawings: a catalogue of drawings in the National Maritime Museum by the elder and the younger Willem van de Velde*, Cambridge, 1958.

The ship is a French two-decker of the same type as those published by Robinson on plate 66, nos. 315 and 316, both of which show French coats of arms. Here the round escutcheon is left blank, but it seems to be encircled by the chain of an order of chivalry, a combination not found on the emblems of Dutch ships. Instead of the seated Justice represented in no. 316, here a woman wearing a crown and holding another escutcheon on her knee sits on the taffrail. The standing female atlantes flanking the coat of arms, however, had occurred already on the stern of the ship *Amalia*, built for the Dutch admiralty in 1637, which had inaugurated a new Dutch type. The present drawing may have been executed in the sixties.

Adriaen van de Velde

Painter and etcher. Born Amsterdam, 1636; died there, 1672.

Adriaen van de Velde

Caspar Netcher

Jan de Bisschop

47 Study of a female nude, partly draped, seen from behind. Inscribed *A. van de Velde. F.*
Black and white chalks on grey paper, 165 × 285 mm.
Inv. no. R.51
Provenance J. Bernard, sale 24 November 1834, D.1, sold for fl. 53.- to Brondgeest; C. Mendes de Leon, not mentioned in sale 20 November 1843; Baron J. Verstolk van Soelen, sale 22 March 1847, no. 263, sold for fl. 51.- to Roos; G. Leembruggen, sale 5 March 1866, no. 659, with another for fl. 8.- to Gruyter for the Teyler Foundation.
Bibliography Scholten, p. 259, R.51.

Most of Adriaen van de Velde's studies after the nude are in red chalk; this one is an exception, also because of its delicate treatment. It may be an early work; less emancipated from the technique used by J. Backer and G. Flinck than the bolder red chalk drawings.

48 A horse, cattle and peasant women in a landscape.
Black chalk with light grey wash, 191 × 279 mm.
Inv. no. R.39
Provenance J. W. Barchman Wuytiers, sale 17 September 1792, H.3, bought for fl. 45.- by Hendriks for the Teyler Foundation.
Bibliography Scholten, p. 255, R.39.

There is a superficial resemblance in the arrangement with the scene in a painting of 1663 in the Mauritshuis, The Hague (catalogue no. 197), but the most that can be said is that the drawing is of about the same date and may possibly represent an early idea for the picture. Van de Velde drew his landscapes in a range of different styles and techniques; this shows his lightest touch.

Caspar Netcher

Painter. Born Heidelberg, 1639; died at The Hague, 1684.

49 A seated lady, richly dressed, bending forward, with both hands on her needlework. A young man looks down at it.
Black and white chalk on blue paper, 357 × 247 mm.
Inv. no. R.79
Provenance H. van Eyl Sluyter, sale 26 September 1814, G.62, bought for fl. 12.10 by Hendriks for the Teyler Foundation.
Bibliography Scholten, p. 267, R.79; Reproduced in Kleinmann's Series.

The lady seems to be occupied with her needlework, but her pose may be compared with that of the mother combing her son in the painting in the Rijksmuseum (catalogue no. 1724) for which the study seems to have been used. A free drawing from Netcher's mature period, when he had abandoned completely the solemn reserve observed by Gerard Terborch, who was his second teacher. From the costume and headdress it may be dated in the second half of the sixties. The young man standing over the woman in the background is so faintly drawn in outline that he can hardly be seen in a reproduction.

On the verso A slight sketch of the bust of a woman, in black chalk.

Jan de Bisschop

Lawyer, amateur draughtsman and etcher. Born Amsterdam, 1628 (or possibly 1629); died at The Hague, 1671.

Jan de Bisschop

Jan van Huysum

Cornelis Troost

50 Fallen trees across an avenue at ter Noot House between The Hague and Voorburg. Signed with the monogram *J E* and dated *1658*; inscribed by the artist on the verso *de Laen van 't Huys ter Noot bij den Haegh.*
Pen and brush with brown ink ('Bisschop-inkt'), 97 × 154 mm.
Inv. no. Q*38
Bibliography Scholten, p. 226, Q*38.

De Bisschop must have filled several small albums with topographical views from different countries and one of them with records of The Hague and its surroundings. As far as we know, all of them were taken apart before the end of the eighteenth century. The date shows that the drawing was made after de Bisschop had witnessed the development of landscape drawing in Rome; he may even have seen Poussin's.

Jan van Huysum

Painter. Born Amsterdam, 1682; died there, 1749.

51 Fruit and vine leaves on a large Delft dish. Signed *Jan van Huizum F.*
Watercolour, 434 × 586 mm.
Inv. no. U*40
Collections Mlle Enschedé; acquired May 1873 for fl. 10.– for the Teyler Foundation.
Bibliography Scholten, p. 406, U*40.

An unusually large watercolour, washed with great freedom, but true to nature. It may be supposed to belong to van Huysum's earlier work, in so far as there is no wish whatsoever to produce a decorative effect.

52 A bouquet of different flowers in a niche.
Black oil, chalk and grey wash, 430 × 304 mm.
Inv. no. T.12
Bibliography Scholten, p. 354, T.12.

The kind of flowers and their arrangement are reminiscent of the picture in the Wallace Collection (no. 149), but the drawing is definitely a variant, that painting in reality being based on a similarly executed study which passed from the C. Otto Collection to that of Mr Lousada, London, who lent it to the Dutch Exhibition at the Royal Academy, 1929 (*Catalogue*, p. 260, no. 720). The year 1726 of the Wallace Collection's flowerpiece cannot, however, be far amiss for the present sheet. Other variants are in the Louvre (reproduced in J. G. van Gelder, *Prenten en Tekeningen*, Amsterdam, 1958, plate 146) and a more careful interpretation of the same theme sold in the C. Otto sale (Leipzig, 7 November 1929, no. 77, with reproduction).

Cornelis Troost

Painter and etcher. Born Amsterdam, 1693; died there, 1750.

53 Scene from the Comedy 'Chrispijn Medicijn'. Signed and dated *C. Troost 1733*. Inscribed above the door *quod* (t?) *tot*, and on the bottle label *olie tobaco.*
Gouache and pastel on blue paper, 345 × 295 mm.
Inv. no. T.28
Provenance The same subject occurs in the sales of D. Muilman (29 March 1773, no. 1212, in black and white, fl 40.50 to Foucquet); W. P. Kops (14 March 1808, D.7, fl. 40.–to

Cornelis Troost

Jacob de Wit

Hendriks); J. de Vos Sr. (30 October 1833, G.7, fl. 86.- to Brondgeest); Baron J. Verstolk van Soelen, sale 22 March 1847, A.14, bought for fl. 160.- by de Vries.
Bibliography A. Ver Huell, *Cornelis Troost en zijn werken*, Arnhem, 1873, p. 110; Scholten, p. 359, T.28.

'Ce dessin d'une exécution vigoureuse, et plein d'expression est un des meilleurs de cet habile artiste, contemporain de W. Hogarth, et dont à juste titre il est considéré comme le rival.' This praise in the Verstolk catalogue seems to be justified. C. Troost owed a large part of his inspiration to the comedies written by a contemporary author J. Langendijk. This time he illustrates a passage in an older play, translated by Pieter de la Croix, 1685, from the French *Crispin Médecin* written by Noël Lebreton, Sieur d'Hauteroche (1630?–1707), published in Paris, 1670.

Chrispijn brings a secret message to the maidservant of a doctor. Not knowing what to do when her master knocks at the door, she urges Chrispijn to lie down on the dissection table and to simulate death. The doctor would have started his dissection if the servant had not appeared as the ghost of the dead man, uttering terrible warnings.

On the verso A black chalk sketch of a maid serving.

54 An evening reception in a sumptuous room. Signed with black chalk on the verso *C Troost*.
Black chalk, pen and brown wash, 411 × 612 mm.
Inv. no. U*52
Provenance ?Baron J. G. Verstolk van Soelen, sale 22 March 1847, no. 623, sold for fl. 1.- to

Brondgeest; A. van der Willigen, sale 12 August 1874, no. 269, sold for fl. 595.- to Fr. Muller; bought privately in March 1880 for fl. 450.- for the Teyler Foundation.
Exhibition Rotterdam, 1946, 'Cornelis Troost en zyn tijd', no. 79.
Bibliography A. Ver Huell, *Cornelis Troost en zijn werken*, Arnhem, 1873, p. 114; Scholten, p. 411, U*52; J. G. van Gelder, *Prenten en Tekeningen*, Amsterdam, 1958, p. 49, 97, plate 143.

The room is rather too big for even the largest private house existing in Amsterdam at the time, and, if not a free invention, it yet cannot be identified. The sparkling effect of the drawing in a way seems to emulate Canaletto and Guardi, whose works Troost can hardly have known.

Jacob de Wit

Painter and etcher. Born Amsterdam, 1695; died there, 1754.

55 Apollo, Minerva and the Muses playing instruments among the clouds. Design for a ceiling painting. Signed *J. de Wit invt*.
Watercolour, 415 × 290 mm.
Inv. no. T.62
Exhibition Rotterdam, 1946, 'Cornelis Troost en zijn Tijd', no. 119.
Bibliography Scholten, p. 370, T.62; A. Staring, *Jacob de Wit*, Amsterdam, 1958, *passim*.

Watercolours like this, beautiful in themselves, were executed by de Wit as finished models for a ceiling to be painted. He may have had some in store to be shown to

Jacob de Wit

Aert Schouman

prospective patrons, and only if they were used, he marked on the back for whose house they had been painted. The present one bears no such inscription. The figures represented are often free inventions difficult to give a name to; in the present case Apollo and Minerva seem to be in the centre, while the helmeted woman holding a spear might be Diana. It is impossible to assign a date to this type of drawing when not inscribed, as de Wit's style had been fully formed and hardly changed since about 1725.

56 Winter, allegorized in a grisaille. One of a pair. Signed *J. de Wit invt.*
Black chalk, washed with grey on a tinted ground, heightened with white, 360 × 228 mm (with margins).
Inv. no. T.56
Bibliography Scholten, p. 368, T.56;
A. Staring, *Jacob de Wit*, Amsterdam, 1958, *passim*.

Pendants like these allegories of the seasons were often painted by de Wit for decorating less conspicuous wall sections in eighteenth-century interiors, such as *supraportes* in rooms, corridors or halls. This pair was used for a pair painted *en grisaille* now preserved in the Kassel Museum (reproduced in Staring 38–9). Another pair of similar drawings was sold at Lucerne, February 1943 (reproduced in Staring 107–08); and one more exists in the Fodor collection, Amsterdam (catalogue 1863, no. 262–63), which is dated 1748, the approximate year of our drawing too. These imitations of stucco work were called *witjes* in Dutch, a play on de Wit's name and the whitewash covering the stucco. One of those in the Amsterdam town hall Sir Joshua

Reynolds called: 'one of the best deceptions (i.e. trompe l'oeil) I have seen.'

57 A winged cherub's head. Signed *J d Wit.*
Black and red chalks, watercolour and pastel on buff paper, 277 × 257 mm.
Inv. no. T.64
Bibliography Scholten, p. 370, T.64.

When Sir Joshua Reynolds painted in 1787 his famous *Angels' Heads* (the subject being Frances Isabella Ker Gordon), now in the National Gallery, he was apparently inspired by drawings by de Wit. The most conspicuous ones are now kept in the Fodor collection, Amsterdam (one pair is dated 1748). De Wit seems to have been the first to develop the theme as a subject in itself, whereas winged heads in a context have existed since the Italian Renaissance and were popular motives in religious paintings of the Bolognese School, for example. De Wit treated them in variations, but only in drawings, obviously meant to enchant the Dutch collectors.

Aert Schouman

Painter and etcher, also on glass. Born Dordrecht, 1710; died at The Hague, 1792.

58 A bunch of poppies.
Watercolour, 413 × 256 mm.
Inv. no. U.28b
Provenance The number of drawings by Schouman preserved at Haarlem makes it probable that groups of them had remained together since the death of the artist and were bought in sets by the Teyler Foundation. The present drawing probably belonged to lot 481 of the Schouman sale on 10 December

Aert Schouman

Jurriaen Andriessen

Wybrand Hendriks

1792, which contained twenty-five sheets with cockscombs, poppies and other flowers, soon afterwards dispersed.
Bibliography Not mentioned by Scholten.

The drawing shows to what extent Schouman was able to develop a free use of watercolour. As such he was unsurpassed by any of his Dutch contemporaries.

59 Pheasants and other birds near the bust of a satyr in a park. Signed *A. Schouman.* Annotated in pencil by the artist on the verso *bruine Pauwies* (i.e. brown female peacock).
Watercolour, 285 × 210 mm.
Inv. no. U.33
Exhibitions Aert Schouman, Dordrecht-Amsterdam, 1960-61, p. 75, no. 119, plate 41.
Bibliography Scholten, p. 384, U.33.

Schouman was a noteworthy specialist in wall-paintings on canvas, several of which are still in existence: the present drawing gives an idea of how he built up his painted scenes. Besides that, he was an outstanding draughts-man of animals and flowers.

Jurriaen Andriessen

Painter. Born Amsterdam, 1742; died there, 1819.

60 A sacrifice in a classical temple in an extensive landscape peopled by shepherds and playing children. Signed and dated on the back *J. Andriessen 1793 inv: et fec:*
Watercolour, 323 × 252 mm.
Inv. no. V.53

Provenance One of a pair bought for fl. 210.- from the artist in 1793.
Exhibition Amsterdam, 1933, Amsterdamsch Historisch Museum, de Waag, 'Het Amsterdamsche Woonhuis', no. 130.
Bibliography Scholten, p. 434, V.53; J. Knoef, *Tusschen Rococo en Romantiek*, Amsterdam, 1943, p. 10.

Jurriaen Andriessen was one of the most successful painters of wall-decorations on canvas of his time, both in the classical tradition formerly represented by Isaac de Moucheron (1670-1740) and in the new manner which was based exclusively on Dutch scenery. The present drawing and its companion piece (not shown here), reflect the older category, but this pair was apparently not meant to be enlarged into a picture, as the Teyler Foundation commissioned a number of similar pairs of pendants from artists considered outstanding, during several years in succession around 1790.

Wybrand Hendriks

Painter and etcher. Born Amsterdam, 1744; died Haarlem, 1831.

61 The head of a boar.
Watercolour, 342 × 495 mm.
Inv. no. W.36
Bibliography Scholten, p. 445, W.36.

Wybrand Hendriks was the most successful of the curators of the art collections of the Teyler Foundation during the first hundred years of its existence. He served it as *opzichter en kastelein* (i.e. surveyor and warden) from 1785 till 1819, when he retired because of bad

Wybrand Hendriks

Isaak Ouwater

health. Under him the Queen Christina drawings were acquired, the oval room was built, and the drawings were mounted and inserted in their beautiful volumes bound in red morocco. Hendriks was one of the best painters of his time and a great draughtsman; the present drawing shows what he was able to perform.

Isaak Ouwater

Painter. Born Amsterdam, 1750; died there, 1793.

62 The fish market at Leyden with the Marekerk in the distance. Inscribed on the verso *de vismarkt te Leyden I*^k *Ouwater*. Watercolour and gouache, 280 × 402 mm.
Inv. no. U.75^a
Provenance One of a pair, acquired in 1793 from the artist; the other is not any more in the Teyler collection.
Bibliography Not described by Scholten; I. Blok in *Oud Holland*, Vol. 34, 1918, pp. 247–55.

The Leyden fish market in its older aspect inspired artists like Jan van Goyen and Jan Steen, but one would not recognise their lively vision in this static late eighteenth-century view, in which the details play such a large part. For a century the new genre had benefited greatly from the art of Jan van der Heyden (1637–1712). The Marekerk had been built from 1639 to 1649 by A. van s' Gravesande, but several of the houses had been rebuilt on a larger scale, and the fountain erected on the design of J. Roman at the end of the seventeenth century, the sculpture being by J. Hannaert (the top) and C. Minee.

On the bridge a sledge drawn by a horse reminds us of that popular means of transport on the cobblestones of Dutch towns. The costumes point to a date towards 1790. Possibly executed in 1793 on a direct commission from the Teyler Foundation.

Italian drawings

Anonymous. Lombard School: late fourteenth century

63 A greyhound.

Tip of the brush over silver-point on parchment, 70 × 88 mm.

Inv. no. K.IX.25

Provenance Queen Christina, etc. (see p. 9)

Exhibitions Amsterdam, 1934, no. 557; Milan, 1958, 'Arte Lombarda', no. 166 or 167; Vienna, 1962, 'Europäische Kunst um 1400', no. 270; Stockholm, 1966, no. 1083.

Bibliography A. van Schendel, *Le dessin en Lombardie jusqu' à la fin du XV siècle*, Brussels, 1938, pp. 60–6, plate 49; Popham and Pouncey, p. 184; R. W. Scheller, *A Survey of medieval model books*, Haarlem, 1963, pp. 143–54.

The same greyhound, wearing the same collar, is represented in a sitting position on another small vellum sheet in the Teyler Museum (van Schendel, plate 48: Scheller, plate 99). The two drawings were originally on one sheet, one above the other. The same dog is shown again in two other drawings. In his standing position he appears in a drawing in the British Museum (van Schendel, plate 43; Popham and Pouncey, p. 184, no. 290, plate 207). Seated, he is found again on one of the leaves of a book of drawings in the Biblioteca Civica at Bergamo. The drawings in this book are mainly of animals and birds, with a few groups of human figures and some emblems and designs for ornament. Such a collection of drawings is sometimes described nowadays as a model book, because it is believed that the drawings, whether drawn from nature or copied from other works of art, were intended to provide artists with a stock of useful motifs. Many medieval drawings are of this type. One of the leaves of the Bergamo book is inscribed *Johininus de Grassis designavit*. The name is that of Giovannino de Grassis, an artist who was active in Milan at the court of the Visconti and in the cathedral during the last years of the fourteenth century. He was probably, among other things, the head of a studio of artists illuminating manuscripts, for whose use the Bergamo book of models may have been compiled. The inscription quoted does not prove that he made any of the drawings himself: indeed there are stylistic variations which suggest that more than one artist was at work. But it is reasonable to suppose that some and perhaps all the drawings were made from his designs.

The related drawings at Haarlem and in the British Museum show how the compilers of model books borrowed from each other. Since there was so much borrowing, it is not easy to determine which drawings are the originals and which are copies. All the drawings discussed here may be copies after lost prototypes. But there is some reason for thinking that the Haarlem dogs are original drawings, made from life and not copied from another drawing. The fact that the *same* dog is studied twice on the same sheet in different positions suggests (though it does not prove) that the artist had a real dog before his eyes and wanted to make a thorough study of it. In the Bergamo and British Museum draw-

Anonymous. Lombard School:
late fourteenth century

Anonymous. North Italian:
about 1400

Anonymous. Italian School:
early fifteenth century

ings the dog shares the sheet with animals of a different kind, as one might expect in a collection of miscellaneous patterns. There is no doubt, moreover, that the Teyler dogs are more accurately observed and more sensitively drawn than the other two, as both van Schendel and Scheller agree. They look altogether more lifelike. As van Schendel suggests, they may be the prototypes which were circulating in the studio of Giovannino de Grassis. Scheller takes the same view. Since Giovannino died in 1398, we can date the drawings approximately. It is rare to find studies of animals so true to life being made at a time when Pisanello was still in his cradle. That power of observation and that preference for drawing from nature rather than from memory or from inanimate models which he introduced into Italian art are foreshadowed here.

Anonymous. North Italian: about 1400

64 Standing saint or allegorical figure.
Brush drawing in brown wash, heightened with white on green prepared paper, 183 × 103 mm.
Inv. no. A.1
Provenance Queen Christina, etc. (see p. 9).
Bibliography van Regteren Altena, p. 42, fig. 41.

Van Regteren Altena sees a reminiscence of Romanesque miniature and fresco painting in the handling of the hair, but is inclined to date the drawing in the last years of the fourteenth century and to situate it in North Italy, perhaps in Padua and the circle of Guariento. Dr Degenhart informs us, in a letter, that he

has classified the drawing provisionally under the school of Bologna. The subject has been called St. Stephen and St. Lawrence, but neither of these saints is normally represented as a clerk holding a bow and arrow; nor is it easy to discover any other saint whom these attributes would fit.

Anonymous. Italian School: early fifteenth century

65 Reclining Madonna suckling her Child, with three flying angels.
Pen and wash on reddish grey paper, 122 × 183 mm.
Inv. no. K.IX.21
Provenance Queen Christina, etc. (see p. 9).
Bibliography van Regteren Altena, p. 40, fig. 13; B. Degenhart and A. Schmitt, *Corpus der italienischen Zeichnungen 1300–1450*, Part I, Vol. 1, p. 254, no. 151, and Vol. 3, plate 184c, Berlin, 1968.

Van Regteren Altena suggests a north Italian origin for this drawing. Degenhart and Schmitt place it in central Italy, comparing the reclining Virgin with a figure in a fresco showing the Hierarchy of Angels in the church of the Annunziata at Riofreddo in Lazio. There is a resemblance between the two figures. The cycle of frescoes at Riofreddo was painted in 1422 by an artist under the influence of Gentile da Fabriano, possibly, as Venturi suggests, by Arcangelo di Cola da Camerino. (See Venturi, Vol. 7, part 1, pp. 159–64; the particular figure in the frescoes is shown in plate 163; also in Degenhart and Schmitt, Part I, Vol. 1, p. 254, fig. 360. See also Venturi's note on Cola da Camerino in *L'Arte*, Vol. 13, 1910, pp. 377–81.)

School of Andrea Mantegna

Vincenzo Foppa

School of Andrea Mantegna

66 The Entombment of Christ.

Pen and ink, 106 × 98 mm.
Inv. no. K.IX.27
Provenance Queen Christina, etc. (see p. 9).
Bibliography van Regteren Altena, p. 42.

There are compositional resemblances between this drawing and two pictures of the Entombment which Professor Ferdinando Bologna believes to be copies of a lost original by Mantegna (see his article 'Ricordi di un Cristo morto del Mantegna' in *Paragone*, Vol. 7, 1956, no. 75, pp. 57–60 and plates 36–7). One of these pictures is in the church of the Annunciata at Angri, near Naples, and the other is in the Gismondi collection in San Remo. Bologna maintains that they are copies of an altarpiece by Mantegna which is described as follows in a letter written by Pietro Summonte, dated Naples, 1524: 'in Santo Dominico, una cona dove è Nostro Signore levato della Croce e posto in Lenzuolo, di mano del Mantegna'. (in S. Domenico, an altarpiece of Our Lord lifted from the Cross and layed on a sheet, by Mantegna).

The man on the right in the drawing corresponds with the man who is holding the sheet in the two pictures: and his left arm is stretched across the Body of Christ in the same way. The position of Christ is very similar in the drawing as in the paintings, so is His relationship to the man who supports Him from behind. There can be little doubt that the drawing is connected with the paintings, though the right hand half of the scene is not shown and has doubtless been cut away. The drawing was formerly attributed to Mantegna, but van Regteren Altena is inclined to see in it the hand of the young Bellini. Though compelling and expressive, it is perhaps a little too stiff and graceless to be by either of them and is more likely to be a record of Mantegna's composition by one of his lesser pupils or followers. There is another drawing by the same hand in the Teyler collection showing the dead Christ supported by putti. It was in the exhibition 'Le dessin italien dans les collections hollandaises', Paris, Rotterdam, Haarlem, 1962, as by Giovanni Bellini (no. 27, plate 27, in the catalogue). See M. Jaffé, *Burlington Magazine*, Vol. 104, 1962, p. 234.

Vincenzo Foppa

Painter. Born Brescia, between 1427 and 1430; died there, 1515 or 1516.

67 Mythological or historical scene.

Pen, 122 × 215 mm.
Inv. no. D.40
Provenance Queen Christina, etc. (see p. 9).
Exhibitions Amsterdam, 1934, no. 546.
Bibliography A. von Schendel, *Le dessin en Lombardie jusqu'à la fin du XVᵉ siècle*, Brussels, 1938, p. 87; F. Wittgens, *Vincenzo Foppa*, Milan, no date, p. 46, footnote 46; van Regteren Altena, p. 46.

The attribution to Foppa, which appears to have originated in the 1934 exhibition catalogue, rests on a comparison with a study in pen and ink for the 'Justice of Trajan' in Berlin, that being one of the few drawings that may be ascribed to Foppa with a fair degree of confidence (van Schendel, fig. 75; Wittgens, plate 22). It is doubtful, however, whether the Teyler drawing is really by the same hand. Neither van Schendel nor Wittgens think that it is. It has a Venetian rather than a Milanese flavour, and is somewhat reminiscent of Carpaccio. The subject of the drawing is not known. It is sometimes given as Mucius Scaevola, but that title hardly fits. A man is admittedly fanning a fire on the right of the sheet, but Mucius appears to be missing from the scene. The youth with an outstretched arm on the left seems to be handing a bowl to the seated man or receiving it from him.

Bernardo Parentino

Also known as Parenzano, Paduan painter. Born at Parenzo in Istria; died at Vicenza, 1531 (aged 94).

68 Triumph of Mars.

Pen, 402 × 278 mm.
Inv. no. K.III.7
Provenance Queen Christina, etc. (see p. 9).
Exhibitions Paris, Rotterdam, Haarlem, 1962, no. 20; Stockholm, 1966, no. 1084.
Bibliography Z. Wazbinski, 'À propos de quelques dessins de Parentino pour le couvent de Santa Giustina' in *Arte Veneta*, Vol. 17, 1963, pp. 23–4, and fig. 19; van Regteren Altena, p. 44.

Formerly anonymous, the drawing was attributed to Parentino by van Regteren Altena, as recorded in the catalogue of the exhibition cited. J. Byam Shaw (in *O.M.D.*, Vol. 9, 1934, pp. 1–7) was the first to collect together a group of drawings that might be attributed to Parentino. Other drawings have since been added to the group. Most of them are mentioned (with bibliographical references) in Wazbinski's article. He connects some of them, including the Haarlem drawing, with Parentino's S. Giustina frescoes in Padua and claims to have thus proved that they are by Parentino. Unfortunately the connection is not very close. Not one of the drawings can be regarded as a study for the frescoes. They merely bear a generic resemblance to the frescoes in style and content. No one has yet published a drawing which can be given to Parentino on irrefragable grounds: nor is it sure that all the drawings now gathered together under his name are by the same artist. The name is nevertheless a convenient one to cover a fairly homogeneous group of Paduan origin. Within the group the Haarlem drawing has the closest affinity with a sheet in the Pierpont Morgan Library, New York, as the authors of the Dutch exhibition catalogue cited point out (see Fairfax Murray Catalogue, plate 80). A peculiarity common to both these drawings and not present or not so marked in any of the others is the strong bias towards elaborate ornamental volutes. Whether he is drawing a shield, the handles of a vase, the wings of a sphinx or the joint plates in a suit of armour, the artist never loses a chance of rolling the edges of the material up into a leathery spiral. This characteristic is absent from certain other drawings which might otherwise seem to be by the same hand, such as the Venus and Cupid in the Victoria and Albert Museum (Byam Shaw, *op. cit.*, plate 7; Wazbinski, plate 25) and the Victory at the British Museum (Wazbinzki, plate 18).

Raffaellino del Garbo

Florentine painter. Born about 1466; died 1524 (according to Vasari).

69 Angel holding up the right side of a mandorla.

Pen and ink, pricked for tracing, 215 × 189 mm.

Raffaellino del Garbo

Michelangelo

Inv. no. A.52
Provenance Queen Christina, etc. (see p. 9).
Bibliography van Regteren Altena, p. 46.

Part of an ornamental design. Formerly kept under the name of Raphael, the drawing was attributed to Raffaellino by van Regteren Altena. As a physical type the angel is typical of the artist and the handling of the pen suggests a comparison with other drawings by him, with the Mater Dolorosa, for example, in the British Museum (1860-6-16-45; Berenson, 641; Popham and Pouncey, 66, plate LXI). The pricked outlines suggest that the drawing is one of those many designs which Raffaellino, according to Vasari, made for embroidery. There used to be a tendency to divide Raffaellino, both as painter and draughtsman, into two or more different artists. Berenson divided the drawings between Raffaellino del Garbo and Raffaellino del Carlo. But in the Italian edition of his book on the drawings of the Florentine painters, 1961, he decides that they are one and the same person, and that the drawings which he ascribed to Carlo are merely the late drawings of Garbo. According to Vasari the embroidery designs were mostly made in later life, when the artist's powers had declined.

Michelangelo

Michelagniolo di Ludovico Buonarroti-Simoni. Painter, sculptor, architect and poet. Born Caprese, 1475; died Rome, 1564.

70 Nude soldier. Inscribed in ink in the bottom right corner *di Bona*.
Black chalk, 404 × 224 mm (cut on all sides).
Inv. no. A.18

Provenance Queen Christina, etc. (see van Regteren Altena, pp. 38-9 for a discussion of the early history of the Teyler Michelangelos).
Exhibitions London, Royal Academy, 1930, no. 524; Paris, Rotterdam, Haarlem, 1962, no. 77.
Bibliography H. P. Bremmer in *Beeldende Kunst*, Vol. 9, 1921-22, no. 34; Marcuard, plate 1; Wölfflin, p. 319; Haendcke, p. 387; Beckerath in *Kunstchronik*, 1901, p. 422; Berenson, no. 1463; E. Steinmann, *Die Sixtinische Kapelle*, Vol. 2, Munich, 1905, p. 595, no. 16 (verso only); W. Köhler, 'Michelangelos Schlachten-Karton' in *Kunstgeschichtliches Jahrbuch des k.k. Central-Kommission für Erforschung und Erhaltung der Kunst- und historischen Denkmale*, Vol. 1, Vienna, 1907, p. 162; E. Jacobsen, critique of Steinmann's book in *Repertorium für Kunstwissenschaft*, Vol. 30, 1907, p. 395; Thode, Vol. 1, pp. 103, 248 (verso), and Vol. 3, no. 253; Knapp, nos. 305 and 306; Brinckmann, nos. 85 and 86; the same, 'Sind die Haarlemer Michelangelo-Zeichnungen Originale?' in *Zeitschrift für bildende Kunst*, Vol. 59, 1925-26, pp. 219-24; Panofsky, pp. 27-32; A. E. Popham, *Italian drawings exhibited at the Royal Academy, 1930*, Oxford, 1931, no. 211; Tolnay, Vol. 1, p. 219, and Vol. 2, p. 181 (verso); Dussler, no. 524; van Regteren Altena, p. 61.

There is a lightly drawn study of a male back on the right of the main figure. The latter is a study for the Battle of Cascina, for the soldier on the right who is helping his comrade to do up his armour. Michelangelo was working on a cartoon of this subject in 1504 and 1505. He was to have painted it in fresco in the Sala del Consiglio of the Palazzo Vecchio in Florence, as a companion to Leonardo's Battle of

Anghiari. Neither picture was ever completed: Michelangelo's was probably never begun and his cartoon, famous in its day, was broken up and destroyed. The best record of the composition (or of a part of the composition) is the grisaille copy at Holkham Hall, Norfolk, which is illustrated in Köhler and several other of the works cited.

The scene represented is a band of Florentine soldiers surprised by the Pisans while bathing on a hot day near Cascina in 1364. The Teyler Museum possesses another black chalk drawing of a male nude for the same composition (A.19: Knapp, 303: Dussler, 525). The two drawings are similar in style and technique, and they were probably made from the same model at the same time. They were generally accepted as by Michelangelo until Brinckmann put forward the idea that they were copies after the cartoon. His opinion is shared by Panofsky, Tolnay and Dussler, but opposed by Berenson. Panofsky proposed an attribution to Perino del Vaga or Giovanni da Udine, which cannot be justified. Brinckmann's main argument is that the drawings are weak in those places which were hidden from sight by other figures in the cartoon, that is to say, so far as the drawing exhibited here is concerned, in the left leg and right ankle, in both the arms below the elbow, and round the waist. Some of these parts are certainly more summarily indicated than the rest of the body, but so is the head, which was not hidden from sight in the cartoon. Far from being weak, the few spare and rapid lines which define these parts show the set of the head and the movements of the limbs with perfect precision. The handling is typical of Michelangelo who, in his preparatory work for the Cartoon, began, at this date, to employ black chalk on a significant scale for figure studies like this.

On the verso A rough compositional sketch in black chalk in a very summary short-hand style showing, from left to right, Judith handing the head of Holofernes to her servant, Holofernes on a bed in an alcove and two figures entering upon the scene. It is a sketch for the subject on the Sistine Ceiling (1508–12). The concise handling is reminiscent of the Oxford sketch-book (Parker, 299–306; Tolnay, Vol. 2, p. 214, no. 28a, figs. 248–50).

71 Studies for a Descent from the Cross.
Inscribed in ink along the upper edge *Di Michel Angelo bona Roti* and lower down on the right side *72*.
Red chalk, 270 × 180 mm.
Inv. no. A.25
Provenance Queen Christina, etc. (see van Regteren Altena, pp. 38–9).
Exhibitions Amsterdam, 1934, no. 594; Stockholm, 1966, no. 1095.
Bibliography Marcuard, plates XIX and (verso) XX; Wölfflin, p. 320; Haendcke, p. 389; Berenson, no. 2480; P. D'Achiardi, *Sebastiano del Piombo*, Rome, 1908, p. 326; Thode, Vol. 3, no. 266 and Vol. 2, pp. 404, 480; Knapp, nos. 330 and 331; Brinckmann, no. 89; Panofsky, 'Die Pieta von Ubeda. Ein Kleiner Beitrag zur Lösung der Sebastiano – Frage', in *Festschrift für Julius Schlosser*, Vienna, 1927, p. 161, footnote 22; Panofsky, p. 49; J. Wilde, 'Zur Kritik der Haarlemer Michelangelo-Zeichnungen' in *Belvedere*, Vol. 11, 1927, p. 142f: W. Stechow, 'Daniele da Volterra als Bildhauer', in the *Prussian Jahrbuch*, Vol. 49, 1928, p. 83; L. Dussler, *Sebastiano del Piombo*, Basel, 1942, p. 190, no. 215; R. Palluchini, *Sebastian Viniziano*, Milan, 1944, pp. 82, 191; Goldscheider, 1951,

no. 89; Goldscheider, 1966, no. 86; Wilde, *B.M. Catalogue*, p. 65; Dussler, no. 529; Tolnay, Vol. 5, p. 217, no. 241; van Regteren Altena, pp. 62–3; C. de Tolnay, 'La Deposizione di Cristo. Disegno attribuito a Michelangelo a Haarlem' in *Pantheon*, Vol. 25, 1967, pp. 20–6, fig. 2.

The drawing in the middle of the sheet showing the composition as a whole is surrounded by five subsidiary studies, in which the artist tries out certain alternatives in the planning of the parts.

The composition of the main drawing is found in a stucco cast of a Deposition in relief traditionally attributed to Michelangelo in the Casa Buonarroti, Florence. The figures on the cross correspond with the drawing, but the figures on the ground are somewhat different and more numerous. The composition shown in the relief must have enjoyed considerable popularity, judging from the number of versions which have survived. There is a gilt bronze version dating from the sixteenth century in the Victoria and Albert Museum, as well as two eighteenth-century versions in stucco and terracotta. At least five other versions are recorded. (They are listed in J. Pope-Hennessy, *Catalogue of Italian sculpture in the Victoria and Albert Museum*, Vol. 2, London, 1964, pp. 434–35, no. 463. The three reliefs in the Museum are nos. 463, 464 and 465 in the same catalogue.)

Another work connected with the drawing is the red chalk drawing in the British Museum known as the Three Crosses. (Wilde, *B.M. Catalogue*, no. 32.) As has long been recognised, the two drawings are obviously by the same hand; and were very likely variant ideas for the same work. The British Museum drawing represents a slightly earlier moment in the story of the Passion, when Christ is still hanging on the Cross between the two thieves. But a ladder has already been erected against the cross and a man is lying on the cross-beam evidently in the act of unfastening Christ's right hand, while another man on the ladder is apparently freeing his feet. At the foot of the cross we see, as in the Haarlem drawing, a huddled group of figures in attitudes of despair. The representation of similar actions in both compositions and the fact that the handling and the general conception of the subject are the same in both prove that the drawings are closely connected.

Both drawings are among those which Berenson thought should be transferred from Michelangelo to Sebastiano del Piombo. But his opinion, though accepted by Knapp, has found little support from other Michelangelo scholars or from the writers on Sebastiano mentioned in the bibliography.

Panofsky, followed by Stechow and Wilde (who afterwards changed his opinion) attributed the drawing to Daniele da Volterra, maintaining that it was a compositional study for his Descent from the Cross in S. Trinità dei Monti, Rome. There is no connection, however, between the drawing and the painting, apart from the subject and such generic resemblances as one might expect to find in two interpretations of the theme made by artists working at the same time, in the same place and in the same iconographic tradition. Daniele could have painted his Deposition without ever having seen the Teyler drawing. Nor is it possible in the light of the information which has been recently assembled on Daniele's drawings to see his hand in this particular sheet. (For a discussion of Daniele's drawing style, see M. Hirst, 'Daniele da Volterra and the Orsini Chapel' in

Burlington Magazine, Vol. 109, 1967, pp. 498–509.) Wilde's latest opinion (as expressed in his *B.M. Catalogue*) is that the drawing is by Michelangelo after all. He suggests that it may be connected with a 'Quadretto per uno studiolo' for Cardinal Domenico Grimani on which Michelangelo is known to have been working in 1523. As it is not known what the subject or the medium was, this conjecture cannot be verified. But as Wilde observes, the subject represented in the Teyler drawing and the Three Crosses was appropriate for a cardinal's study. He considers, moreover, that the style is consonant with the date. Goldscheider dates the drawing in the early 1530s, comparing it with the Fall of Phaethon in the British Museum, which can be dated 1534 (Frey, 57; Goldscheider, 94; Dussler, 177) and with some of the sketches for the Last Judgment, which were made in 1534 and 1535. Tolnay, who holds to the view that Michelangelo may have made the drawing for Daniele's Descent from the Cross, which was not begun before 1541, necessarily dates the drawing later, towards 1540. The evidence in favour of so late a date is weak, once it is admitted that there is no connection with Daniele's picture. It is certainly difficult to find analogous drawings that can be dated so late, whereas there are certain earlier analogies, beginning with the drawings made for Sebastiano del Piombo in 1516 in the British Museum. The Teyler drawing, together with the Three Crosses, seems to occupy a position mid-way between the Sebastiano drawings and the drawings made for Tommaso de Cavalieri in the early 1530s.

The verso shows three heads and a woman in voluminous draperies bending down to lift or arrange something with her hands. The figure is not connected with any known work of Michelangelo's, but it may belong to the same Deposition as the drawings on the recto. As Wilde first observed, the heads are copied from Giotto's fresco showing St. Francis appearing before Brother Augustine and the Bishop of Assisi in the Bardi Chapel, S. Croce, Florence. The heads are those of the monks on the extreme left in the group round Brother Augustine and of the two figures in the foreground on the left. The drawings were attributed by Berenson to Pietro Urbano: by Knapp to Sebastiano del Piombo: and by Panofsky to Daniele da Volterra. Brinckmann, Goldscheider and Dussler do not accept them as by Michelangelo. Thode and Wilde suggest that Michelangelo drew the female figure and that the heads are by a pupil, an opinion which would probably command a good measure of assent among scholars today.

72 Seated male nude and a woman hoeing or reaping.

Pen, 207 × 232 mm.
Inv. no. A.17
Provenance Queen Christina, etc. (see van Regeteren Altena, pp. 38–9).
Bibliography Marcuard, plate XXIV; Wölfflin, p. 319; Berenson, no. 1473; Thode, Vol. 3, no. 270; D. Frey, *Michelangelo. Quellen und Forschungen*, Berlin, 1907, p. 22, no. 10; Knapp, nos. 307 and (verso) 307a; Brinckmann, no. 92; Panofsky, pp. 34–5; M. Delacre, 'Some Michelangelo drawings' in *Burlington Magazine*, Vol. 66, 1935, p. 284; A. E. Popham, Letter in *Burlington Magazine*, Vol. 67, 1935, p. 45; Dussler, no. 523; W. McAllister Johnson, 'Primaticcio revisited: aspects of draughtsmanship in the School of

Fontainebleau' in *Art Quarterly*, Vol. 29, 1966, pp. 245–68, fig. 15.

Most of the scholars cited exclude the drawing from the Michelangelo canon, but it is accepted by Berenson and Knapp. Berenson describes it as 'a delightful early sketch no later than the bathers' (1504–05). Knapp dates it during the Sistine ceiling period (*c.* 1508–12). The drawing is typical of Michelangelo, but has attracted adverse criticism because the figure of the bending woman corresponds closely with a figure of Ceres reaping corn painted by Primaticcio in the Ball Room of the Palace of Fontainebleau (1552–66). A drawing by Primaticcio showing the figure of Ceres is reproduced in L. Dimier, *Le Primatice*, Paris, 1928, plate XI. Panofsky and Dussler argue from the resemblance between the two figures that both the drawings on the Teyler sheet are by a member of Rosso's circle in Fontainebleau. McAllister Johnson attributes them to Primaticcio. But the drawings by Primaticcio with which he compares the bending woman are manifestly by a different hand. The male nude on the same sheet bears even less resemblance to any known drawing of Primaticcio's. There is, of course, a connection between Primaticcio's Ceres and the bending woman in the Teyler drawing. If Primaticcio did not draw the figure in the Teyler drawing, then he must have copied it, or borrowed his figure from another similar drawing. The second alternative is doubtless the correct explanation. The Ceres in Primaticcio's drawing is strongly reminiscent of Michelangelo, not only in build and pose, but in the hang of her draperies too. The drapery is hardly indicated in the Teyler drawing. It follows that Primaticcio must have taken his figure from

another drawing by Michelangelo showing the same figure, and it must have been a more developed drawing, now lost. Mr Michael Hirst has suggested (orally) that Rosso Fiorentino may have been the intermediary channel between Michelangelo and Primaticcio. He was on friendly terms with Michelangelo in the 1520s and may have copied or even possessed some of his drawings, which Primaticcio might have seen subsequently when working with Rosso at Fontainebleau. Another possibility, touched upon by van Regteren Altena, is that the Teyler sheet may have been one of those Michelangelo drawings which Antonio Mini took to France early in the 1530s (van Regteren Altena, pp. 38–9). The drawing may be dated, somewhat conjecturally, since we have nothing but the style to go on, in the 1520s or perhaps a little earlier. The sketch of the bending woman is in the same manner as another rapid outline pen drawing in the Casa Buonarroti (Frey, 211b; Dussler, 279; Barocchi, 45). This drawing of a sarcophagus with a statue of the defunct on the lid, is probably connected with the third project for the tomb of Julius II and may thus be dated about 1516.

On the verso Two studies of a left foot in pen and ink. Not by Michelangelo.

73 Studies for Christ on the Cross and other figures. Inscribed in ink at a later date as follows: in the top right corner *50:* towards the bottom right corner *No. 87:* in the bottom left corner *di Bona Roti.* There are various pen scribbles in the lower part of the sheet, including three capital *A*s on the left side. Black chalk, 331 × 299 mm.
Inv. no. A.34

Michelangelo

Provenance Queen Christina, etc. (see van Regteren Altena, pp. 38–9).
Exhibitions Stockholm, 1966, no. 1093.
Bibliography Marcuard, plates XXII (and XXIII verso); Wölfflin, p. 320; Berenson, no. 1675; T. Ashby, 'Drawings attributed to Andreas Coner' in *Papers of the British School at Rome*, Vol. 2, 1904, p. 8; Thode, Vol. 2, pp. 473–74, and Vol. 3, no. 269; Knapp, nos. 332 and (verso) 333; Panofsky, p. 57; Delacre, pp. 311, 315; Popham and Wilde, p. 266, no. 260; Goldscheider, 1951, no. 112; Goldscheider, 1966, no. 106; Dussler, no. 299; Tolnay, Vol. 5, p. 172, nos. 157 and (verso) 158.

Apart from the main study of a Christ on the Cross, there are four other drawings on the sheet: on the left side a detail of Christ's right knee and a torso in profile: on the right side another torso in profile, possibly a study of the same figure of Christ viewed from the side; and underneath the faint outlines of a head in profile.

Most of the scholars listed accept the drawing as by Michelangelo, but Berenson rejects it as 'too stringy and fumbling'. Knapp and Panofsky share his view. The same figure of the crucified Christ occurs in a drawing in Windsor Castle and in another in the Louvre. They are reproduced in Popham and Wilde no. 460, fig. 105, and in Tolnay, Vol. 5, fig. 325. They are usually regarded as copies after a lost original by Michelangelo. The Teyler drawing is presumably a study for that original. The composition is not connected with any known work by Michelangelo in painting or sculpture. But as de Tolnay has observed, a small bronze Crucifix in the Metropolitan Museum, New York (Tolnay, Vol. 5, fig. 327), described as a copy after

Michelangelo since 1937, corresponds approximately with our drawing, though reversed. The drawing is dated by de Tolnay 1530–34. But Goldscheider, Dussler and Wilde place it, more convincingly, in the period when Michelangelo was planning and painting the Last Judgment in the Sistine Chapel, that is to say, between 1535 and 1540. Some of the black chalk drawings for that work are in a similar style, notably another drawing (of a male nude) in the Teyler Museum (Knapp, 322; Dussler, 295).

Michelangelo was at that time under the influence of Vittoria Colonna, who turned his thoughts towards religion and inspired him to make several drawings of sacred subjects, including a Crucifixion in the British Museum (Frey, 287; Dussler, 329; Wilde, *B.M. Catalogue*, 67).

On the verso Several designs for sections of mouldings in red chalk: overlapping with these, a tracing of the largest study on the recto, and two slight sketches of a man walking, all in black chalk.

74 Aeneas and Dido with a putto. On the left side an inscription in ink mostly cut away and illegible.
Black chalk, 180 × 136 mm.
Inv. no. A.32
Provenance Queen Christina, etc. (see van Regteren Altena, pp. 38–9).
Bibliography Marcuard XVIII(b) and (recto) XVIII(a); Berenson, no. 1470; Thode, Vol. 3, no. 265, and Vol. 2, p. 161; Knapp, nos. 328 and 329; J. Wilde, 'Zur Kritik der Haarlemer Michelangelo–Zeichnungen' in *Belvedere*, Vol. 11, 1927, p. 142ff; Panofsky, p. 49; W. Stechow, 'Daniele da Volterra als Bildhauer' in *Prussian Jahrbuch*, Vol. 49, 1928, p. 83, and

Michelangelo

Daniele da Volterra

footnote 3; Delacre, pp. 210, 451, and (recto) p. 452; Goldscheider, 1951, no. 185 and (recto) no. 123; Goldschieder, 1966, no. 116 and (recto) no. 115; Wilde, *B.M. Catalogue*, p. 114, footnote no. 1; Dussler, 297; Tolnay, Vol. 5, no. 209 (verso) and no. 215 (recto).

The side exhibited is the *verso*. The figures are drawn over some sketches of architectural details. The young man in the foreground is undressing with the help of a putto. A pentimento, very lightly drawn, shows the putto on the other side of the young man. Behind him a reclining figure on a bed. Wilde was the first to observe that the two figures in the foreground correspond with the figures of Aeneas and a putto in a picture, by (or after) Daniele da Volterra discovered by Hermann Voss in a Swedish private collection (p. 133, fig. 2, in Wilde's article: see also Voss's article on the picture in *Kunstchronik*, Vol. 34, 1922, pp. 375ff). The subject of the picture is Mercury commanding Aeneas to leave Dido. He appears in the air above Aeneas's head and Aeneas is shown looking up at him. Mercury is missing in the drawing, perhaps because the sheet has been cut.

Wilde attributed the drawing at first to Daniele, but as he writes in the catalogue cited above, he has since become converted to Berenson's view that Michelangelo made it for Daniele. According to Berenson 'it has all the dynamic ponderousness of the aged Michelangelo, as well as his tricks and mannerisms of notation at that period'. Wilde dates it about 1556: Tolnay about 1545, observing that the male nude is stylistically close to the soldier on the left in the Conversion of St. Paul. Wilde's date is more likely to be correct. The picture was commissioned by Giovanni della Casa, who after four years in

Venice returned to Rome in 1555. When he died in 1556, the picture was recorded as incomplete in his house (see S. H. Levie, *Der Maler Daniele da Volterra*, doctoral dissertation for Basel University, Cologne, 1962, pp. 130–32).

Count Antoine Seilern has another very similar drawing in black chalk by Michelangelo showing Aeneas and the putto alone (Tolnay, Vol. 5, no. 210; formerly in the V. Bloch collection). The British Museum has a black chalk drawing in Daniele's own hand for the painting (1956–10–13–13).

On the recto The principal drawing is a figure of a saint meditating over a book in black chalk, in the same late style. Tolnay, following Thode, suggests that it is a design for one of the painted niche figures that were to have decorated the dome of St. Peter's. But Wilde is probably right in supposing that the drawing is connected with Daniele's sculptures in S. Pietro in Montorio, Rome. The marble figure of St. Paul may well have been derived from Michelangelo's drawing, though it has none of the drawing's force. If this supposition is correct, then both sides of the Haarlem sheet contain drawings made by Michelangelo for Daniele da Volterra.

Daniele da Volterra

Daniele Ricciarelli, painter and sculptor. Born Volterra, about 1509; died Rome, 1566.

75 Portrait of Michelangelo.
Black chalk, 295 × 220 mm. The corners cut off. Pricked for transfer.
Inv. no. A.21
Provenance Queen Christina, etc. (see p. 9).

Daniele da Volterra

Raphael

Bibliography E. Steinmann, *Die Portraitdarstellungen des Michelangelo*, Leipzig, 1913, pp. 48–9, plate 47; S. H. Levie, 'Die portretten van Michelangelo door Daniele da Volterra', in *Nederlands Kunsthistorisch Jaarboek*, Vol. 6, 1955, pp. 119–31; S. H. Levie, *Der Maler Daniele da Volterra* (doctoral dissertation, Basel University), Cologne, 1962, pp. 152–54, 188.

The drawing, which is pin-pricked for tracing along all the principal lines, is a cartoon (or part of a cartoon) for the portrait of Michelangelo which Daniele da Volterra inserted into his fresco of the Assumption of the Virgin in the Della Rovere Chapel, in S. Trinità dei Monti, Rome. Michelangelo is represented in the fresco as one of the Apostles who witnessed the Assumption. The head in the drawing is of the same size as the one in the fresco. Altena points out that some of the hatching lines are horizontal, from which he deduces that the head when originally drawn was vertical, a position in which the hatching lines run obliquely in the natural way. It is reasonable to assume that Daniele made the drawing from life, and afterwards set it at an angle so as to use it in the fresco. The frescoes in the della Rovere chapel were probably finished by 1555 and cannot have been begun before 1548, that being the year when Lucrezia della Rovere (who commissioned them) became the owner of the chapel. The portrait therefore shows Michelangelo (b. 1475) between the ages of 73 and 80. The fresco being much damaged, the drawing is now the best record of Michelangelo's features as they appeared to his friend Daniele.

Levie (in the article cited) sees another, earlier portrait of Michelangelo by Daniele in the figure of Fabius delivering a speech in a painting in the Palazzo Massimo alle Colonne, Rome. After Michelangelo's death his nephew Lionardo commissioned Daniele to make the well-known bronze portrait, which exists in various versions.

Raphael

Raffaello Santi, painter, architect and sculptor. Born Urbino, 1483; died Rome, 1520.

76 Standing putto.

Black chalk heightened with white, 338 × 190 mm.
Inv. no. A.57
Provenance Queen Christina, etc. (see van Regteren Altena, pp. 53–4).
Exhibitions Amsterdam, 1934, no. 631; Paris, Rotterdam, Haarlem, 1962, no. 66.
Bibliography Passavant, Vol. 2, p. 460, no. 300; A. Venturi, 'Disegni di Raffaello nei Musei Teyler di Haarlem e Wallraf-Richartz di Colonia', in *L'Arte*, Vol. 24, 1921, pp. 19–23; O. Fischel, *Raphael*, London, 1948, pp. 89, 363, plate 99; L. Salerno, 'Il profeta Isaia di Raffaello e il putto della Accademia di S. Luca' in *Bolletino d'Arte*, 4th series, Vol. 45, 1960, pp. 81–96; M. Jaffé, 'Italian drawings from Dutch Collections' in *Burlington Magazine*, Vol. 104, 1962, p. 233; J. Shearman, 'Raphael's unexecuted projects for the Stanze' in *Walter Friedlaender zum 90. Geburtstag. Eine Festgabe . . .*, Berlin, 1965, p. 173; van Regteren Altena, p. 53; the same, in *Openbaar Kunstbezit*, Vol. 12, 1968, pp. 38–8b (with reproduction).

The drawing was used for a figure of a putto which fills a ceiling pendentive above the Attila fresco in the Stanza d'Eliodoro in the Vatican. In the fresco, as in the drawing, the boy holds in his right hand a large ring set with a diamond and entwined with three feathers, a device of Leo x (1513–21). Fischel ascribes the fresco to Raphael's assistant Giovanni Francesco Penni, but the drawing to Raphael himself. The Medici emblem points to a date soon after March 1513, when Leo x was elected Pope and the decorations of the Stanza, initiated by Julius ii, were nearing completion. The putto is closely related to another putto, the one who stands on the left side of the Prophet Isaiah in Raphael's fresco in S. Agostino, Rome, probably painted in 1512. Instead of holding a diamond ring, this boy's right arm hangs loosely down by his side entwined with a festoon of flowers, and he supports a sculptured tablet on his left shoulder. Otherwise the figures are very similar. The putto in the Isaiah fresco occurs again in a fragment of a fresco in the Academy of S. Luca in Rome. Though this fragment was generally accepted in the past as a Raphael, Salerno maintains, with considerable cogency, that Raphael was not accustomed to make facsimiles of his own works and that the putto in the Academy is a copy, probably made by Jean-Baptiste Wicar, who bequeathed it to the Academy (1834).

77 Two horsemen and a man running.

Red chalk, 247 × 242 mm.
Inv. no. A.78
Provenance Queen Christina, etc. (see van Regteren Altena, pp. 53–4).
Exhibitions Amsterdam, 1934, no. 628; Paris, Rotterdam, Haarlem, 1962, no. 65.
Bibliography Passavant, Vol. 2, p. 460, no. 299; Crowe, Vol. 2, p. 281; Dollmayr, p. 261, note 2; E. Müntz, *Les tapisseries de Raphael au Vatican*, Paris, 1897, p. 15; P. Oppé, 'Right and left in Raphael's cartoons' in *Journal of*

the Warburg and Courtauld Institutes, Vol. 7, 1944, p. 91; M. Jaffé, 'Italian drawings from Dutch Collections' in *Burlington Magazine*, Vol. 104, 1962, p. 233; van Regteren Altena, p. 52; Dussler, *Raphael*, p. 113.

It is a study for three figures in the lost cartoon of the tapestry representing the Conversion of St. Paul. It shows the two horsemen and the man running in the foreground of the tapestry. The set of ten cartoons illustrating some of the acts of the Apostles was commissioned by Leo x. The tapestries, woven in Brussels, were intended to hang in the Sistine Chapel in the Vatican. The cartoons were probably completed in 1516. The seven which survive belong to H.M. the Queen and are on exhibition in the Victoria and Albert Museum. The Conversion of St. Paul is among the three which have been lost, but the composition is preserved in tapestry. The Haarlem drawing, like all the studies for the cartoons, is in the same direction as the cartoon, that is to say in the opposite direction to the tapestry, which was automatically reversed in the weaving. The figures correspond fairly closely with the figures in the tapestry, but the running man is shown in a shirt and drawers instead of a loose tunic, and more of the nearest horseman's leg is visible than in the tapestry. There is a similar drawing at Chatsworth in the collection of the Duke of Devonshire on a rather worn and damaged sheet (inv. no. 905. Courtauld Institute, Photographs of the Chatsworth drawings, no. 800: see also the Catalogue of the Exhibition at Burlington House, London, 1969, 'Old Master Drawings from Chatsworth', no. 60, plate 60). The two drawings are so alike that one of them must be a copy, perhaps even a tracing, of the other. Passavant describes the Teyler version as 'un dessin magistral' and omits the Chatsworth drawing from his list of Raphaels in the Duke's collection. On the other hand Crowe and Cavalcaselle, Dollmayr and Dussler regard the Teyler drawing as a copy. Fischel does not refer to it, but he, like Dollmayr, ascribes the Chatsworth sheet to Raphael's assistant G. F. Penni. It is unlikely that anybody has had an opportunity of placing the two drawings side by side. But a comparison of photographs suggests that the Teyler drawing is the original. The Chatsworth drawing is more evenly executed, with shallower modelling and fewer accents. The shallow modelling is particularly noticeable in the arms of the horsemen, where the hatching is placed in exactly the same places as in the Haarlem drawing, without however giving that impression of knotted muscles which the Haarlem version conveys. The lack of accents is most noticeable in the hair of the man on foot. In the Chatsworth sheet the hair is a formless mop which would hardly be recognisable as a part of a human body, were it cut out and seen in isolation. In the Teyler drawing, on the other hand, the curls in the hair and the windswept wisps in the nape of the neck are crisply and economically rendered with a few accented strokes of the crayon. The whole drawing has more life and energy.

On the verso A black chalk drawing, heightened with white, showing Pope Julius II kneeling in prayer at a faldstool. It is a study for the Mass of Bolsena, in the Stanza of Heliodorus in the Vatican, completed in 1512.

78 Studies of two figures, half length.
Red chalk, 600 × 224 mm.

Inv. no. A.68
Provenance Queen Christina, etc. (see van Regteren Altena. pp.53–4).
Exhibitions Amsterdam, 1934, no. 630; Paris, Rotterdam, Haarlem, 1962, no. 69.
Bibliography M. Jaffé, 'Italian drawings from Dutch collections', in *Burlington Magazine*, Vol. 104, 1962, p. 233; van Regteren Altena, p. 52; Dussler, *Raphael*, p. 108.

The right-hand figure was used, with some changes, to represent Psyche presenting Proserpina's vase to Venus in the ceiling fresco of the Villa Farnesina, Rome, completed in 1519. In the fresco the right arm is extended to hold the vase, and the left hand is placed a little higher on the girl's breast: but in other respects the fresco corresponds closely with the drawing. The other figure on the sheet does not seem to be connected with any known composition by Raphael: nor does it appear to have any compositional relation with the Psyche figure: Raphael would hardly have repeated the same gesture with the left hand twice in the same picture. As van Regteren Altena suggests, the drawings look as though they had been made from the life from the same model, probably a boy. The complete scene of Psyche presenting the vase to Venus is studied in a quick pen sketch in the Ashmolean Museum, Oxford, and in a carefully finished red chalk drawing in the Louvre. They are both reproduced in F. Haitt, *Giulio Romano*, New Haven, 1958, plates 39 and 43: and in J. Shearman, 'Die Loggia der Psyche in der Villa Farnesina und die Probleme der letzten Phase von Raffaels graphischem Stil' in the *Vienna Jahrbuch*, 1964, N.S. Vol. 24, 1964, pp. 59–99, plates 79 and 81. It is surprising that the Teyler drawing has not received more attention from

Raphael

Polidoro Caldara da Caravaggio

Giulio Romano

Raphael scholars, considering its beautiful quality. If the criteria proposed by Shearman in the article quoted are applied to it, it is by Raphael rather than Giulio Romano, to whom some modern critics, notably Hartt, are inclined to ascribe most of the red chalk drawings for the Farnesina.

Polidoro Caldara da Caravaggio

Painter. Born Caravaggio (Lombardy), between 1490 and 1500; died Messina, ?1543.

79 The Virgin and Child crowned by two angels.
Red chalk, squared in black chalk, 197 × 162 mm.
Inv. no. B.94
Provenance Queen Christina, etc. (see p. 9).

Attributed to Polidoro by Philip Pouncey. The crisp and incisive strokes of the sharply pointed chalk pencil are typical of the artist and so is the feeling of compactness and solidity which they convey. The purpose of the drawing is not known. It is reminiscent of a drawing in the British Museum which shows the Virgin and Child in a similar pose (Pouncey and Gere, no. 215, plate 185).

Giulio Romano

Giulio Pippi, painter and architect. Born Rome, about 1499; died Mantua, 1546.

80 Neptune in a chariot drawn by sea horses.
Pen and wash, 210 × 328 mm.
Inv. no. A.X.50

Provenance Queen Christina, etc. (see p. 9).
Bibliography F. Hartt, *Giulio Romano*, New Haven, 1958, p. 296, no. 155; van Regteren Altena, p. 59.

As Hartt states, the drawing is a study for one of the small inset paintings in the ceiling of the Sala dei Venti in the Palazzo del Te, Mantua. The ceiling is illustrated in Hartt, fig. 192. The drawing corresponds closely with the painting and shows the whole composition of the scene, not just a part of it. The Sala dei Venti was decorated between September 1527 and March 1528. The scheme is shown in a diagram in Hartt, p. 118. Piera Carpi attributes the execution of the painting of the Neptune panel to Girolamo da Pontremoli, one of Giulio's assistants in the Palazzo del Te ('Giulio Romano ai servigi di Federico II Gonzaga' in *Atti e Memorie della R. Accademia Virgiliana di Mantova*, N.S., 11–3, 1918–20, p. 49).

As Professor van Regteren Altena has observed (in a letter), Giulio's design is similar to Marcantonio Raimondi's well known engraving *Quos Ego* (Bartsch 102). In the print, as in Giulio's composition, Neptune stands in a large sea-shell drawn by sea-horses whose long snake-like tails writhe in a similar way. It has never been decided whether the engraving is after Raphael or Giulio. It is certainly not an engraving of the Teyler drawing, but it may be after a variant design by Giulio, or the general idea may have been taken from the Teyler drawing.

81 The arms of Cardinal Ercole Gonzaga.
Pen and ink and wash, 417 × 277 mm.
Inv. no. A.X.64
Provenance Queen Christina, etc. (see p. 9).
Bibliography F. Hartt, *Giulio Romano*, New

Giulio Romano

Correggio

Haven, 1958, pp. 251, 253; p. 308, no. 363; van Regteren Altena, p. 60.

The shield and the cardinal's hat are carried on high by winged putti, while a woman personifying Wisdom and holding a scroll and a rudder drives a chariot harnessed to four eagles. The scroll is lettered *Renovabitur ut aquilae juventus*, a quotation from Psalm 103, verse 5: 'who satisfieth thy mouth with good things; so that thy youth is renewed like the eagles.' A drawing at Chatsworth is similar in many respects, except that there is no lettered scroll and a putto brandishing a lance takes the place of the woman in the chariot (Hartt, *op. cit.*, no. 362, plate 518). The two drawings were doubtless alternative designs for the same occasion; but it is not known what the occasion was. The four eagles harnessed to the chariot are obviously an allusion to the four eagles in the Gonzaga arms. The device most often used by Cardinal Ercole Gonzaga was an eagle fighting with a swan, with the motto *Sic repugnant*, or alternatively an eagle fighting with two swans, with the motto *Tantum lacessitus et vincit*. (See C. Padiglione, *Le divise dei piu illustri personaggi della Casa Gonzaga*, Naples, 1864, p. 11.) Hartt dates the drawing late in Giulio's life, after 1540 when Ercole became regent on the death of his brother Federico II.

Correggio

Antonio Allegri, painter. Born Correggio, between 1489 and 1494; died there, 1534.

82 Eve and a putto with an apple.
Red chalk strengthened with pen, 127 × 130 mm.

Inv. no. A.X.67
Provenance Queen Christina, etc. (see p. 9).
Exhibitions Paris, Rotterdam, Haarlem, 1962, no. 99.
Bibliography Venturi, Vol. 9, Part 2, p. 579, fig. 476; A. Venturi, *Correggio*, Rome, 1926, p. 297, fig. 151; C. Ricci, *Correggio*, London, 1930, p. 176, fig. 278b; A. E. Popham, *Correggio's drawings*, London, 1957, pp. 72, 160, no. 52, plate 60a; van Regteren Altena, p. 66; A. E. Popham, *Italian drawings . . . in the British Museum, Artists Working in Parma in the sixteenth century*, London, 1967, p. 8.

It is a study for the figure of Eve in the fresco showing the Assumption of the Virgin in the dome of Parma Cathedral (about 1526–30). In the fresco Eve's head is shown rather more in full face and tilted back a little more. Moreover, her left arm is extended and holds the apple, instead of hanging loosely down. She is surrounded by heads of angels, but none corresponds with the putto in the drawing. The drawing therefore is an early idea for the figure in the fresco. A drawing in the British Museum (Ricci, *op. cit.*, plate 279, and Popham, *Correggio's drawings*, plate 61) resembles the Teyler drawing closely; and Popham suggests that the Teyler drawing was partly traced from it, that being a method of working out a theme sometimes used by Correggio. But the head in the Teyler drawing is rather more full-face. A later study, which shows the figure of Eve almost exactly as executed, is in the Louvre (Ricci, *op. cit.*, plate 278a; Popham, *op. cit.*, plate 60b).

On the verso A rough sketch in chalk showing a round window, part of a balustrade and a seated figure: probably, as Popham suggests, an early sketch for the lower part of the fresco in Parma Cathedral (see Popham, *Correggio's drawings*, pp. 68–70, plate 62b).

Schiavone

Andrea Meldolla, painter and etcher. Born Zara, about 1503; died Venice, 1563.

83 Three drawings of goddesses. Each of them inscribed *Tintoretto*.
Pen and wash, 165 × 70 mm. each.
Inv. no. K.IX.32, a, b and c.
Provenance Queen Christina, etc. (see p. 9).
Bibliography van Regteren Altena, pp. 82–6, figs. 53–5.

A figure of Minerva is the subject of two of the drawings: the third represents Urania holding a globe. The figures were evidently intended to be framed in niches. The drawings are traditionally attributed to Tintoretto, but van Regteren Altena sees more of Schiavone than Tintoretto in the handling. The old attribution to Tintoretto, he suggests, may go back to the time in the late 1540s when Tintoretto was under Schiavone's influence and occasionally collaborated with him. Both artists were employed in Sansovino's Libreria in Venice. Among the pictures that have survived are two philosophers standing in niches by Schiavone, probably painted soon before his death in 1563: and several similar figures by Tintoretto. They were painted for the principal room of the Library. (See D. von Hadeln 'Beiträge zur Tintorettoforschung' in the *Prussian Jahrbuch*, Vol. 32, 1911, pp.25–58, plates 2 and 3: also Berenson, *Venetian School*, plates 1182 and 1304–05.) Schiavone's philosophers are somewhat similar to the goddesses in the drawings in pose and proportions, and one of them holds a globe in his arms, like Urania in the drawing. There is no evidence, however, that Schiavone painted any female figure in this room, though he may possibly have done so in another part of the building.

We know from the documents quoted by von Hadeln that Tintoretto and a little known artist called Domenico Molin were working on some paintings for the Vestibolo of the Library before and after 1562, and van Regteren Altena suggests that the drawings may possibly have some connection with those works, which have been lost. We should have to suppose, in that case, that Schiavone or another artist made the drawings, because it is hard to see the hand of the mature Tintoretto in them. This assumption does not conflict with the evidence, because the contract quoted by Hadeln states that the artists must work from drawings that shall be given to them. Until, however, we find out what the subjects of the pictures were, the question whether the drawings are connected with them or not must remain a matter of conjecture. Three other drawings in the Teyler Museum, each showing a Virtue in a niche, are possibly by the same hand and may belong to the same series. In van Regteren Altena's opinion, they are somewhat nearer to Schiavone's known drawings. They are illustrated in van Regteren Altena, p. 83, fig. 52.

Possibly by Lelio Orsi

Painter, architect and designer. Born at Novellara (probably), 1511; died there, 1587.

84 Jonah thrown to the whale.
Tip of the brush and various shades of brown

Possibly by Lelio Orsi

Attributed to Veronese

wash, heightened with white on brown paper, 212 × 194 mm.
Inv. no. B.1
Provenance Queen Christina, etc. (see p. 9).
Bibliography van Regteren Altena, pp. 56–7.

The traditional attribution to Perino del Vaga though not altogether impossible, is not very convincing. Van Regteren Altena tentatively suggests the name of Maturino on the strength of an entry in an inventory of drawings in the Odescalchi Collection, dated 1713. The inventory is described in van Regteren Altena, p. 22. The entry (no. 1373) reads: 'Altro disegno in carta a chiaro scuro rappresenta Nave con figurine del Maturino con Cornicetta liscia.' As we do not know any drawings by Maturino (Polidoro's shadowy colleague), and as the inventory description is not exact enough to enable us to identify the drawing with any degree of certainty, the idea must remain an interesting conjecture. Meanwhile Mr Philip Pouncey has observed (in conversation) that the handling seems to point in the direction of Lelio Orsi. The writhing waves, the theatrical light effects, the atmosphere of storm and stress, the agitated movements of the figures are all certainly reminiscent of him. The drawing contains all the ingredients which Venturi associated with him: 'contorsioni spasmodiche, . . . arrovalementi turbinosi, . . . guizzi da lampi, . . . la furia dei venti' (Venturi, Vol. 9, part 6, p. 623). The characteristic handling of the waves may be compared with the handling of the clouds supporting some of the figures in a design by Orsi for the decoration of the façade of his own house in Novellara. The drawing is in the Estense Gallery, Modena (inv. no. 1265) and is illustrated in R. Salvini and A. M. Chiodi, Catalogue of the Lelio Orsi

Exhibition, Reggio Emilia, 1950, p. 112, no. 14, fig. 14.

Attributed to Veronese

Paolo Cagliari, painter. Born Verona, about 1530; died Venice, 1588.

85 An Allegory: Venice crowned by Victory.
Pen and brown wash, heightened with white, on blue paper, oval, 289 × 204 mm.
Inv. no. B.40
Provenance Queen Christina, etc. (see p. 9).
Bibliography van Regteren Altena, p. 87; W. Vitzthum, Review of van Regteren Altena in *Master Drawings*, Vol. 4, 1966, p. 304.

The drawing is inscribed at 25 different points with initial letters in red chalk to indicate colours. As van Regteren Altena has observed, it corresponds fairly closely with an oval ceiling painting by Palma Giovane in the Sala del Gran Consiglio in the Doge's Palace in Venice. The picture, one of Palma's most ambitious works, represents Venice crowned by Victory, and was painted between 1578 and 1584 (illustrated in Venturi, Vol. 9, part 7, p. 194, fig. 194). The drawing, however, is not by Palma. Van Regteren Altena attributes it to Veronese. Veronese painted another oval ceiling picture in the same room, a pendant to Palma's picture, showing the Apotheosis of Venice, and van Regteren Altena suggests that Veronese may have been commissioned to make designs for both pictures. Vitzthum's view, on the other hand, is that the drawing is probably a copy after the picture, rather than a design for it. Two other drawings of the same subject are recorded.

Attributed to Veronese

Federigo Barocci

Lodovico Carracci

One is in the collection of Mr C. R. Rudolph (Tietze, 1015, plate 179; described as a first idea for the painting by Palma): the other is in the Uffizi, Florence (W. Heil, 'Palma Giovane als Zeichner' in the *Prussian Jahrbuch*, Vol. 47, 1926, p. 62, fig. 7: Tietze, A.911; Anna Forlani, Catalogue of the *Mostra di disegni di Jacopo Palma il Giovane*, Florence (Uffizi), 1948, no. 10, fig. 5). Heil published the Uffizi drawing as a compositional sketch by Palma, but Tietze and Forlani agree in considering the Rudolph drawing to be by Palma and the Uffizi sheet to be a copy. The Teyler drawing corresponds most closely with the picture. The other two drawings differ from the picture in several respects, but agree with each other so closely that the Uffizi drawing may well have been copied from Mr Rudolph's.

Federigo Barocci

Painter. Born Urbino, about 1535; died there, 1612.

86 Studies of a recumbent baby.
Red and black chalk, 152 × 157 mm.
Provenance Queen Christina, etc. (see p. 9).
Bibliography van Regteren Altena, p. 92.

Erroneously ascribed to Domenico Maria Canuti in the past, with a companion drawing also in red and black chalk, showing a seated child (van Regteren Altena, fig. 65). The attribution to Barocci is due to van Regteren Altena. There are two similar red and black chalk studies of a reclining infant on a sheet in Professor Altena's own collection. (H. Olsen, *Federigo Barocci*, Copenhagen, 1962, p. 197,

fig. 93b.) They, and the kneeling figure of a woman on the same sheet, are connected with the painting of the Nativity in the Prado. The Teyler drawing may be connected with the same or another Nativity.

On the verso Two slight sketches in red and black chalk of a woman leaning over a table or possibly a cradle.

Lodovico Carracci

Painter and etcher. Born Bologna, about 1555; died there, 1619.

87 Designs for caryatids and a border to frame a fresco.
Pen and wash over black chalk, 160 × 347 mm.
Inv. no. c.16
Provenance Queen Christina, etc. (see p. 9).

Caryatids or terminal figures of this type were used by the Carracci to punctuate the narrative scenes in the two friezes which they painted in the Palazzo Fava in Bologna and in a third frieze in the Palazzo Magnani. The drawing is most nearly related to the frieze in the Sala di Enea in the Palazzo Fava. It is probably a preparatory study for it. But when the artist came to paint the fresco, he relieved the figures of the heavy loads which they are represented as bearing in the drawing and painted them in less constrained attitudes. There is a fine black chalk study for one of the terminal figures in the frieze in H.M. the Queen's Collection at Windsor Castle (R. Wittkower, *The drawings of the Carracci . . . at Windsor Castle*, London, 1952, no. 3). The frieze was probably painted soon after 1584,

Lodovico Carracci

Pietro Facini

Attributed to Guido Reni

Domenichino

and is mostly the work of Lodovico without much help from Annibale or Agostino. For a general account of the work and a recent bibliography, see Anna Ottani, *Gli affreschi dei Carracci in Palazzo Fava*, Bologna, 1966. The Aeneas frieze is engraved by Giuseppe Maria Mitelli under the title *L'Enea vagante*, Bologna, 1663.

On the verso Another study of a kneeling caryatid, back view, in black chalk partly strengthened in pen and ink.

Pietro Facini

Painter and etcher. Born Bologna, 1562; died there, 1602.

88 St. Francis kneeling.
Black chalk on buff paper, 495 × 295 mm.
Inv. no. K.1.31
Provenance Queen Christina, etc. (see p. 9).
Bibliography van Regteren Altena, p. 110, fig. 90.

An etching by Facini of St. Francis receiving the infant Christ from the Virgin Mary is connected with this drawing (Bartsch, 1). The pose of the saint is similar, though reversed. According to P. Masini, *Bologna perlustrata*, Bologna, 1666, p. 52, a painting of this subject was one of a pair of pictures by Facini on each side of the high altar in the Church of the Capuccini del Monte Calvario, Bologna; and Nagler (Vol. 4, p. 215) states that the etching is after the painting. The monastery having since been converted into a villa (Villa Revedin), the present whereabouts of the picture is not known. Giovanni Marangoni

was unable to trace it in 1910 (see his article on Facini in *L'Arte*, Vol. 13, 1910, p. 461).

Attributed to Guido Reni

Painter and etcher. Born Calvenzano, 1575; died Bologna, 1642.

89 A woman holding up an offering attended by a page. Inscribed on the mount in an old hand *Guido Reni*.
Red chalk, 240 × 182 mm.
Inv. no. C.39
Provenance Francesco Carretti (Lugt 432a); Queen Christina, etc. (see p. 9).

There is a similar figure in Guido's painting 'The Triumph of Job', since 1796 in Notre Dame, Paris (illustrated in C. Gnudi, *Guido Reni*, Florence, 1955, plate 147). The picture was painted in 1622. Notwithstanding this resemblance, the drawing is hardly typical of Reni and may be a copy.

Domenichino

Domenico Zampieri, painter. Born Bologna, 1581; died Naples, 1641.

90 Head of a priest.
Black chalk heightened with white on grey paper, 317 × 225 mm.
Inv. no. I.42
Provenance Queen Christina, etc. (see p. 9).

The drawing is a study for the head of the priest administering the Sacrament in the famous Last Communion of St. Jerome in the Vatican Pinacoteca. The altarpiece, which is

Domenichino

Giovanni Lanfranco

Guercino

dated 1614, was commissioned for the church of S. Girolamo della Carità, Rome. There are more than fifty other studies for the painting, mostly in black chalk, in the Royal Library at Windsor Castle (see J. Pope-Hennessy, *The Drawings of Domenichino in the collection of His Majesty the King at Windsor Castle*, London, 1948). They are mostly, like this and other Domenichino drawings in the Teyler Museum, in black chalk on grey paper, a favourite medium of the artist between the years 1612–17, but not much used by him subsequently.

Giovanni Lanfranco

Painter. Born Parma, 1582; died Rome, 1647.

91 Two seated women.
Black and white chalk, 245 × 381 mm.
Inv. no. E.18
Provenance Queen Christina, etc. (see p. 9).
Bibliography J. Bean and W. Vitzthum, 'Disegni del Lanfranco e del Benaschi', in *Bolletino d'Arte*, Vol. 46, 1961, p. 108, fig. 6.

The drawing is published by Bean and Vitzthum as a study for two reclining goddesses in Lanfranco's fresco 'The Assembly of the Gods' on a ceiling in the Villa Borghese, Rome, painted in 1624 (illustrated in Paola della Pergola, *Villa Borghese*, Rome, 1962, plate 190). The pose of the woman on the right is unchanged in the fresco: the woman on the left turns her head a different way. Plate 5 in Bean and Vitzthum's article shows a compositional study for the fresco in the Albertina, Vienna (inv. no. 2818). They state also that there is a replica of the Teyler drawing, in reverse, in the Capodimonte Museum, Naples (inv. no. 498).

92 Allegorical figure.
Black and white chalk on brown paper, 408 × 285 mm.
Inv. no. F.32
Provenance Queen Christina, etc. (see p. 9).
Exhibitions Paris, Rotterdam, Haarlem, 1962, no. 152; Stockholm, 1966, no. 1115.
Bibliography J. Bean and W. Vitzthum, *op. cit.* under no. 91, pp. 111, 119, fig. 21; van Regteren Altena, pp. 112–13.

As Bean and Vitzthum have observed, the figure occurs in two frescoes by Lanfranco: first, in Santi Apostoli, Naples, in the nave, above the second window on the left, where it appears (reversed) as one of a pair of allegorical figures flanking a medallion (before 1640): and, secondly, in S. Carlo ai Catinari, Rome, on the right side of the absidal arch, again reversed (1646–47). In the Capodimonte Museum, Naples, there are two more studies of the same figure (see R. Causa, *Lanfranco ai Santi Apostoli*, Naples, 1964, p. 27, nos. 57 and 60).

On the verso Full face study of a woman's head, looking up, in black chalk. Inscribed in pencil *G. Lanfranck*.

Guercino

Giovanni Francesco Barbieri, painter and etcher. Born Cento, 1591; died Bologna, 1666.

93 Two studies of seated Prophets or Evangelists.
Black chalk, 190 × 163 mm.
Inv. no. H.50
Provenance Queen Christina, etc. (see p. 9).

The lower drawing seems to be connected with a St. John the Evangelist by Guercino, in a private collection in Vicenza (discussed and illustrated in Stefano Bottari, 'Una serie di Evangelisti del Guercino', in *Arte antica e moderna*, Vol. I, 1958, pp. 38–40, fig. 18a). The figure is reversed in the drawing, as it often is in Guercino's preparatory studies, but the pose is alike in both works. In the picture as in the drawing, the seated Saint is shown with his head propped on his hand gazing upward with a visionary expression, holding between the thumb and forefinger of his other hand the pages of a book (in the picture) or a scroll (in the drawing). The picture, with its pendant St. Mark in the same collection, probably belongs, according to Bottari, to a set of four Evangelists which Guercino painted for Domenico Fabri in 1623 (see Malvasia, *Felsina Pittrice*, Zanotti edition, Vol. 2, Bologna, 1841, p. 260).

94 The Martyrdom of St. Lawrence.
Pen, 175 × 250 mm.
Inv. no. H.38
Provenance Queen Christina, etc. (see p. 9).
Bibliography D. Mahon, Catalogue of the drawings in the Guercino Exhibition at Bologna, 1968, p. 119, no. 120.

It is an early study for the altar-piece in Ferrara Cathedral (illustrated in N. B. Grimaldi, *Il Guercino*, Bologna, 1968, plate 163). The picture was painted in 1629 for Cardinal Lorenzo Magalotti, who was appointed Bishop of Ferrara in that year. The Saint faces to the right in the picture and not to the left as in the drawing. The executioners and spectators are also rather differently placed, and the kneeling man with the bellows in the drawing is omitted from the painting. Another difference between the two compositions is that the drawing seems to be conceived horizontally, in landscape format, whereas the painting is in the usual upright altar-piece format and the figures are pressed closer together. Notwithstanding these differences, there is undoubtedly a connection between the two works, for in each the Saint lies in the same position, propped on his elbows, with his hands on his chest and his knees raised. The drawing, which is hastily executed, and experimental in character, clearly belongs to an early stage in the evolution of the composition. A drawing in Milan of a man working a pair of bellows was probably made on the same occasion, as Mahon observes (see A. Emiliani, Catalogue of the *Mostra di disegni del seicento emiliano nella Pinacoteca di Brera*, Milan, 1959, p. 54, fig. 74). Another compositional sketch for the same work in the Teyler Museum was in the Guercino exhibition at Bologna, 1966 (Mahon, *op. cit.*, no. 120, fig. 120). Three other drawings identified by Mahon as connected with the commission are in the Statens Museum for Kunst at Copenhagen, in the Louvre (inv. no. 6875) and (in 1915) in a private collection in Leipzig (H. Voss, *Archiv für Kunstgeschichte*, Vol. 2, 1915, plate 146).

95 Landscape.
Pen, 175 × 263 mm.
Inv. no. H.108
Provenance Queen Christina, etc. (see p. 9).

Guercino's landscape drawings are hard to date and can seldom be connected with a painting, but this one is reminiscent in mood of his early landscape pictures. The best account of the subject is in the catalogue by Mahon cited under no. 94, pp. 178–85.

Guercino

Pietro da Cortona

School of Pietro da Cortona

There is a fine collection of more than 100 Guercino drawings in the Teyler Museum. They are doubtless from Queen Christina's collection, like most of the Italian drawings in the Museum. She may have bought some of them from the artist when she visited his studio (according to Malvasia) in 1655. But it is more likely that she bought them after his death from his heirs the Gennari, because there are some school drawings in the collection, which Guercino would not have sold to the Queen. (See Mahon, *op. cit.*, pp. 8–9.)

Pietro da Cortona

Pietro Berretini, painter and architect. Born Cortona, 1596; died Rome, 1669.

96 Sketch for part of a ceiling.
Black chalk, 198 × 408 mm.
Inv. no. J.13
Provenance Queen Christina, etc. (see p. 9).
Exhibitions Paris, Rotterdam, Haarlem, 1962, no. 165.
Bibliography van Regteren Altena, 123.

The principal figure in this rapid sketch is a woman holding a caduceus and walking on clouds, accompanied by another woman holding a key, and by a seated figure wearing a crown, possibly Jupiter. On a lower level two sea-horses attended by nereids, and a group of figures holding up a helmet and some spears or arrows. In the background on the right an angel, goddess or allegorical figure subduing a band of vices or malefactors.

Van Regteren Altena suggests that the drawing shows an early stage in the planning of the ceiling of the Salone in the Palazzo Barberini, Rome. The oblong shape of the sheet would be appropriate for the scenes in the deep cove of the ceiling. He connects it with the scene on one of the short sides of the ceiling showing Pallas Athene subduing the forces of evil (Briganti, plate 131). Another possibility, more in accord with the widely extended composition, is that it is related to the painting on one of the long sides which shows five allegorical female figures, two of whom carry keys, while another holds a caduceus (Briganti, plates 128 and 129). The lower part of the painting shows War subdued by Peace on the right, and the Forge of Vulcan on the left. The right part of the drawing might be interpreted to fit this scheme, but the left side bears no relation to the painting as executed. The ceiling was painted 1633–39.

On the verso A fragmentary sketch of a reclining figure apparently intended for the left side of a cove or vault. It has some affinity with the reclining Venus who acts as a counterpart to Bacchus on one of the longer sides of the Barberini ceiling (Briganti, plate 126).

School of Pietro da Cortona

97 The Birth of the Virgin.
Pen and brown wash on light brown paper, 233 × 176 mm.
Inv. no. K.87
Provenance Queen Christina, etc. (see p. 9).
Bibliography van Regteren Altena, p. 123.

The drawing seems to be by a provincial follower of Cortona rather than by the master himself.

Anonymous. Roman School:
mid-seventeenth century

Gianlorenzo Bernini

Anonymous. Roman School: mid-seventeenth century

98 The Mocking of Christ.
Pen and brown wash, touched with blue wash
and Chinese white; on blue washed paper,
245 × 245 mm.
Inv. no. D.36
Provenance Queen Christina, etc. (see p. 9).

Formerly attributed to Pietro da Cortona. It
is not by him, but his influence is perceptible.
Among his pupils and followers, Romanelli
is the artist whose drawing style approaches
most nearly to this drawing. The leaning
figure of Christ with his right arm across his
body was doubtless inspired by the corre-
sponding figure in Titian's two similar
paintings of the same subject in the Louvre and
in the Alte Pinakothek, Munich.

Gianlorenzo Bernini

Sculptor, architect and painter. Born Naples,
1598; died Rome, 1680.

99 An Allegory of the Blood of Christ.
Inscribed in ink in an old hand *Cav. Bernini*.
Inscribed also on the back in ink *Incidatur. fr.
P. Monardus M[agister] ca[merae] Soc[ius]
S[ancti] Rev[erendissi]mi P[atris] M[agistri]
S[acri] P[alatii] A[postolici]*.
Pen and wash, 386 × 248 mm.
Inv. no. D.10
Provenance Queen Christina, etc. (see p. 9).
Exhibitions Paris, Rotterdam, Haarlem, 1962,
no. 166; Stockholm, 1966, no. 1146.
Bibliography Filippo Baldinucci, *Vita di Gian
Lorenzo Bernini*, 1682, edited by S. S. Ludovici,
Milan, 1948, p. 135; H. Brauer and R. Witt-
kower, *Die Zeichnungen des Gianlorenzo
Bernini*, Berlin, 1931, pp. 166–68, plate 198;
V. Martinelli, 'I disegni del Bernini' in
Commentari, Vol. 1, 1950, p. 103; van Regteren
Altena, p. 23; M. and M. F. dell'Arco,
Bernini, Rome, 1967, no. 228.

The inscription on the back is a licence to
engrave given by Padre Monardo, who was
Papal Censor from 1663 to 1673. The
engraving by Francesco Spierre is illustrated in
Brauer and Wittkower, *op. cit.*, plate 198. It is
a faithful interpretation of the drawing. The
two inscriptions engraved on it help to explain
the subject. The first is a quotation from the
Epistle to the Hebrews (IX, 14) referring to the
purifying virtue of Christ's blood. The second
is a passage from the writings of S. Maria
Magdalena dei Pazzi, who died in 1607 and
was canonized in 1669. It reads: 'Vi offerisco il
sangue dell'umanato Verbo, o Padre Eterno:
e se manca cosa alcuna, l'offerisco a Voi, O
Maria, accioche lo presentiate all'Eterna
Trinità'. The subject of Bernini's composition
is a Crucifix suspended in the air over a
boundless sea of blood. God the Father,
accompanied by angels, watches the sacrifice
from above, and the Mother of Christ tries to
catch in her hands some of the blood which
pours from her Son's wounds, in order to
offer it to God.

Brauer and Wittkower reject the old
attribution to Bernini and suggest that the
drawing is by Baciccio, a view which will
not lack support. The Dell' Arcos, on the
other hand, maintain that it is 'almost
certainly' by Bernini, and Martinelli seems to
be of the same opinion. The documentary
evidence in favour of Bernini's authorship is
strong. Not only does the papal *Incidatur* on
the back of the sheet suggest that this very

Gianlorenzo Bernini

Pietro Testa

drawing was used for the engraving, but we also find the ambassador of the Duke of Modena in Rome informing his master, in a letter dated (subsequently) 1671, that Bernini himself made the drawing for the engraving and had it engraved in his (Bernini's) presence. The Italian text (as published by Imparato in *Archivio Storico dell' Arte*, Vol. 3, 1890, pp. 142–43) reads as follows:

'Il pensiero glié parso bellissimo, e molto utile per tutti; stante questo ha fatto il presente disegnio, et in sua presenza l'ha fatto intagliare per poterne dare a molti ...' Baldinucci's testimony is to the same effect. Bernini, he writes, was in his last years much given to meditating on the Blood of Christ, 'nel quale sperava di affogare i suoi peccati. A tale oggetto disegnò di sua mano e poi fecesi stampare un immagine di Cristo Crocefisso ...'

Baldinucci states in the same passage that Bernini had a large picture painted of the subject which hung at the foot of his bed till his death. Martinelli identifies it with an altar-piece in S. Francesco at Palestrina (V. Martinelli, 'Le pitture di Bernini', in *Commentari*, Vol. 1, 1950, p. 103). There is a small painting of the subject in the collection of the Giocondi family in Rome, to whom it has descended by inheritance from Bernini. Another small painting of the subject was in the Leon Dufournay collection. It is lot 8 in the sale catalogue by M. H. Delaroche, 1819. A copy of the drawing in black chalk was in the Vivant Denon collection and is engraved (in reverse) in the *Monuments des arts du dessin ... recueillis par le Baron Vivant Denon*, Vol. 2, Paris, 1892, plate 112. A sheet in the volume of Bernini drawings at Leipzig (Brauer and Wittkower, 128) shows a composition which foreshadows the theme of the Teyler drawing.

Christ seated beside the Cross shows the wounds in his hands to God, while the Virgin shows Christ the breast which nurtured him. This is a theme which goes back to the fifteenth century (see E. Panofsky, 'Imago Pietatis' in *Festschrift für Max. J. Friedländer*, Leipzig, 1927, pp. 261–308).

The Teyler drawing was probably made after the canonization of S. Maria Magdalena in 1669 and must have been made before 1673 when Monardo ceased to be Papal Censor. The date 1671 on the Modenese legate's letter, though added subsequently, is probably therefore correct.

Pietro Testa

Known as il Lucchesino, painter and etcher. Born Lucca, 1612; died Rome, 1650.

100 **The Holy Family,** beside a pyramid, with a swarm of cherubs.
Pen and wash, 190 × 295 mm.
Provenance Queen Christina, etc. (see p. 9).

The drawing is not connected with any etching by Testa or with any known painting. Miss Karin Hartmann, who is working on a doctoral dissertation on Testa at the Courtauld Institute, London, and has kindly discussed the Teyler drawings with us, believes that it belongs, stylistically, to a type of drawing which Testa was producing in the late 1630s. A number of drawings connected with Miss Armide Oppé's painting of the Adoration of the Shepherds are of this type and reveal an affinity with the Teyler sheet. Among these drawings is a sheet in the Ashmolean Museum, Oxford (Parker, p. 481, no. 957); another in the Graphische Sammlung, Munich (negative no. 2392); and a third in the Pierpont Morgan Library (IV,180.D). It is possible, Miss Hartmann suggests, that the Teyler drawing may be a preparatory study for the lost 'Madonna con S. Giuseppe e putti' recorded in Cassiano dal Pozzo's collection (in the inventory published by F. Haskell and Sheila Rinehart in *Burlington Magazine*, Vol. 102, 1960, pp. 318–27, under no. 11).

101 Two draped figures and a putto in a pendentive or spandrel. In the right margin a small sketch of a woman's bust. Inscribed in pencil *P. Testa.*
Pen and brown wash over black chalk, heightened with white, on blue paper, 303 × 224 mm.
Inv. no. B.88
Provenance Queen Christina, etc. (see p. 9).
Bibliography Exhibition catalogue 'Dessins romains du XVII siècle. Artistes italiens contemporains de Poussin', Paris (Louvre), 1959, no. 47; W. Vitzthum, review of the exhibition in the *Burlington Magazine*, Vol. 102, 1960, pp. 75–6.

The Teyler Foundation has (in B.89) a companion piece, closely similar in subject, style and medium, obviously another design for the same project. There is, as Mr Jacob Bean states in the exhibition catalogue cited, a third design belonging to the same series in the Albertina, Vienna (F. Wickhoff, *Die italienischen Zeichnungen der Albertina*, in *Vienna Jahrbuch*, Vol. 13, part 2, 1892, S.R. 1085): and this, as Miss Hartmann has kindly shown, was etched in reverse by Giovanni Cesare Testa (Nagler, Vol. 18, p. 270, no. 12). Another etching by the same artist shows a fourth design by Pietro Testa, very similar to the third. According to Bean there are, moreover, two old facsimiles

of similar drawings by Testa in the Bibliothèque Nationale, Paris. All these drawings are clearly designs for the same decorative scheme, involving the pendentives of a dome or possibly the spandrels of a row of arches. But such records as we possess of Testa's works do not enable us to identify the project. Bean convincingly associates the drawings stylistically with a lunette-shaped drawing by Testa in the Louvre representing the vision of a saint, no. 47 in the catalogue cited. Miss Hartmann has come to the conclusion that Testa was drawing in this manner in the early 1640s. The Louvre lunette, Miss Hartmann believes, is connected with frescoes, no longer extant, in S. Maria dell'Anima, Rome, executed probably between 1642 and 1644. Another example of a drawing of this period instanced by Miss Hartmann is a study in the Teyler collection (B.86) for Testa's most celebrated Roman altar-piece, the 'Vision of St. Angelo' in S. Martino ai Monti, which was painted in 1645. In handling there is a decided affinity between this study and the drawing shown here.

On the verso a slight sketch in black chalk of the Virgin and Child in a medallion, surrounded by angels' heads.

Bartolomeo Biscaino

Painter and etcher. Born Genoa, about 1632;
died there, 1657.

102 Virgin and Child.
Brush and brown wash heightened with white
on dark red paper, 320 × 255 mm.
Inv. no. K.I.37
Provenance Queen Christina, etc. (see p. 9).

Formerly anonymous and attributed tentatively to Biscaino by van Regteren Altena.
The attribution is somewhat uncertain, but
it situates the drawing in the right environ-
ment, in Genoa, in a circle of artists who
knew Castiglione and felt the influence
of Parmigianino.

Bartolomeo Biscaino

French drawings

Claude Lorrain

Claude Gellée. Born Chamagne, Lorraine, 1600; died Rome, 1682.

103 View of St. Peter's, Rome, and the Castel S. Angelo from Monte Vaticano.
Pen and brown wash, 116 × 185 mm.
Inv. no. L.21
Provenance Possibly Queen Christina, etc. (see p. 10).
'*Bibliography* Scholten, p. 5, L.21; E. Knab, Die Anfänge des Claude Lorrains' in *Vienna Jahrbuch*, Vol. 56, 1960, pp. 110–11, plate 146; van Regteren Altena, p. 26, plate 6; Chiarini, no. 16; Roethlisberger, *Claude drawings*, p. 88, no. 42, plate 42.

By drawing a line on a map from the Castel S. Angelo through the south-east corner of St. Peter's we discover that the artist must have been standing behind the Basilica close to the site of the modern Vatican wireless station, but just outside the wall, which appears in the foreground. Knab and subsequently Roethlisberger are doubtless right in stating that the tower on the south end of the façade is the wooden bell tower erected in 1628 and removed when Bernini's tower (soon afterwards to be demolished) was begun in 1637. It is sometimes said that Bernini's tower is shown in the drawing. But his tower was built of stone, whereas the tower in the drawing is manifestly of wood and (though temporary) complete in itself, since it contains a set of bells. The drawing, therefore, was made between 1628 and 1637. Another drawing by Claude of St. Peter's in the British Museum (Roethlisberger, *Claude drawings*, 452) shows Bernini's tower, as it was between 1641 and 1647. Views, like these, of modern, as opposed to antique, Roman buildings are rare in Claude's oeuvre.

The Teyler Museum possesses one of the largest and finest collections of Claude drawings in the world. Of the thousand drawings by him which are estimated to be extant, nearly a hundred are there. Their provenance is uncertain. They may have belonged to Queen Christina, as most of the Italian drawings in the Museum probably did; but there is no proof. The question is discussed in van Regteren Altena, pp. 22–5 and in Roethlisberger, *Claude drawings*, pp. 69–70.

104 A clearing in a wood. Inscribed in ink *30* in the bottom right corner, the number being written with the sheet turned up on its right side. Signed on the back in red chalk *Clao Ro.I.V.*
Pen and pale brown wash, 200 × 297 mm.
Inv. no. L.15
Provenance Possibly Queen Christina, etc. (see p. 10).
Exhibitions Paris, Petit Palais, 1925, 'Le paysage français de Poussin à Corot', no. 470; Amsterdam, 1926, 'Rétrospective d'art français', no. 155; London, 1932, Royal Academy, 'French Art', no. 585; Paris, Brussels, Rotterdam, 1949–50, 'Le dessin français de Fouquet à Cezanne', no. 40; Amsterdam, 1951, 'Het Franse Landschap', no. 178; Hamburg, 1958, 'Französische Zeichnungen', no. 39; Milan, 1960, 'Il disegno francese', no. 40; Bologna, 1962,

'L'ideale classico . . .', no. 206; Paris and Amsterdam, 1964, no. 5.
Bibliography Scholten, p. 4, L.15; Hind, *Claude drawings*, p. 27, plate 11; J. Valléry-Radot, *Le dessin français au XVIIe siecle*, Lausanne, 1953, p. 194, no. 66, plate 66; Kitson, pp. 73–4, plate 76; Chiarini, no. 24; Roethlisberger, *Claude drawings*, p. 201, no. 474.

The drawing is not connected with any known picture and is manifestly a study from nature, one of the most brilliant Claude ever made, according to Roethlisberger. The number 30 written sideways shows, as Kitson first observed, that the drawing belongs to a distinct group of drawings, all in landscape format and similarly numbered. They obviously formed part of a book of drawings compiled and numbered by Claude himself. Kitson calls it Book B. He gives the name Book A to another series of drawings which are mostly in an upright format. He dates the drawings in Book B about 1640, partly on stylistic grounds and partly because a view of St. Peter's in the series can be so dated from the architectural evidence. Roethlisberger discusses and amplifies Kitson's hypothesis in his *Claude Lorrain; the drawings*, Berkeley and Los Angeles, 1968, pp. 59–63. He renames Kitson's Book A the 'Campagna book' and his Book B the 'Tivoli book', from the subjects which predominate in each. Another drawing from the Tivoli book is exhibited here under no. 105.

105 Rocky landscape with an artist sketching. Signed on the back in red chalk, *Clao R.IV*.
Pen and wash (grey, brown and pink) over a black chalk sketch, 210 × 303 mm.

Inv. no. L.13
Provenance Possibly Queen Christina, etc. (see p. 10).
Bibliography Scholten, p. 3, L.13; Kitson, p. 254; Roethlisberger, *Claude drawings*, p. 202, no. 481, plate 481.

Like no. 104 in this catalogue (q.v.) the drawing belongs to the book of drawings compiled by Claude named 'Book B' by Kitson and the 'Tivoli book' by Roethlisberger. It dates therefore from the early 1640s. The artist appears to be looking across the valley from Tivoli. As Kitson has suggested (in conversation), the building seen on the other side of the ravine is doubtless the one seen from Tivoli in the distance in a drawing in the Hermitage, Leningrad (Roethlisberger, *Claude drawings*, 572, plate 572). That drawing is a study for a painting in H.M. the Queen's Collection (Roethlisberger, *Claude paintings*, no. 89, plate 169). The same (or a similar) house is visible in the painting.

106 Fishing boats near the shore.
Pen and grey and brown wash, 225 × 218 mm.
Inv. no. L.35
Provenance Possibly Queen Christina, etc. (see p. 10).
Bibliography Scholten, p. 8, L.35; Hind, *Claude drawings*, p. 30, plate 32; M. Roethlisberger, *The drawings of Lorrain*, Alhambra, California, 1968, unnumbered plate; Roethlisberger, *Claude drawings*, p. 180, no. 398.

According to Roethlisberger, the incisive penwork compares with a drawing of huts on the shore of Lake Nemi also in the Teyler Museum (Roethlisberger, *Claude drawings*, no. 410). As that drawing belongs to the Campagna book (described under no. 104) and may consequently be dated about 1638–40, we have a conjectural date for the drawing of boats. The boats look as though they had been drawn from life and as though they were on the sea rather than on a river or lake.

107 Samuel annointing David King of Israel.

Pen and wash, with some touches of watercolour over black chalk, on two sheets pasted together in the centre, 196 × 571 mm.
Inv. no. L.103
Provenance Possibly Queen Christina (see van Regteren Altena, pp. 22 ff).
Bibliography Roethlisberger, *Claude paintings*, Vol. 1, pp. 211–12; Roethlisberger, *Claude drawings*, p. 213, no. 522, plate 522.

The drawing is not listed in Scholten among the other Teyler Claudes and was first recognised as a Claude by van Regteren Altena among the anonymous drawings. Roethlisberger confirms the attribution. It is, as he states, a preliminary study for the figures in the picture in the Louvre (inv. no. 315: Roethlisberger, *Claude paintings*, no. LV.69, plate 141. No. 18 in the exhibition 'The Art of Claude Lorrain' at the Hayward Gallery, London, 1969.) The composition of the painting is given on p. 69 of the Liber Veritatis, the book in which Claude made drawings after most of his works as a record. An inscription on the back of the sheet in the Liber Veritatis shows that the picture was painted for Cardinal Giorio, a close friend of Urban VIII and an important early patron of Claude. He ordered seven or eight pictures from Claude between 1638 and 1643, one of them being the Annointing of David.

The Teyler drawing, according to Roethlisberger, is one of the two largest figure studies drawn by Claude. It is not easy to determine at what stage in the composition of the picture the drawing was made, because though it corresponds closely with the picture at certain points, notably in the figures of Samuel and David and in the action of the man holding the goat, the drawing contains absolutely no suggestion of the spacious and airy landscape which is the setting for the scene in the painting. The figures in the painting are scattered across the middle distance in three widely separated groups. In the drawing they are compressed together in the foreground in a compact unbroken frieze, with scarcely any indication of a background. Claude was clearly aiming here at a strictly classical composition based on Roman sculptured friezes. In his classical mood he even borrowed from Raphael, the greatest exponent of classical design among the moderns. As Roethlisberger observes, several of the figures in the drawing are inspired by the fresco of the same subject designed by Raphael in the Vatican Loggia. The figure of David is copied exactly, and when he came to paint the picture, Claude altered the figure of Samuel to bring it, too, more into line with his Raffaelesque model. But in dissolving the dense frieze of figures he weakened, perhaps intentionally, the effect of classical force and gravity created, doubtless as an experiment, in the drawing.

108 Mount Parnassus.

Pen and pale brown wash in foreground and middle distance; chalk and grey wash in the background, 182 × 240 mm.
Inv. no. L.18

Claude Lorrain

Antoine Watteau

Provenance Possibly Queen Christina, etc.
(see p. 10).
Exhibitions Paris and Amsterdam, 1964,
no. 15.
Bibliography Scholten, p. 4, L.18; Roethlisberger, *Claude paintings*, pp. 80, 453;
Roethlisberger, *Claude drawings*, p. 409,
no. 1113, plate 1113.

On the back of the sheet are two drafts of
letters written by Claude to relatives in
Chamagne, his birthplace. They are
reproduced in Scholten, p. 4, and in
Roethlisberger, *Claude drawings*, plate 1131d.
Roethlisberger (*op. cit.*, p. 409) discusses
their meaning (which is somewhat obscure)
and the facts that can be deduced from them
about Claude's family. They have no direct
bearing on the drawing on the recto, but as
they are dated 1679 and 1681, they provide
good evidence for dating the drawing. The
drawing, as Roethlisberger states, is a study
for a painting dated 1681, done for Prince
Colonna, now in the Boston Museum of Fine
Arts (Roethlisberger, *Claude paintings*, p. 451,
L.V.193, plate 314). Five other drawings,
connected with the same commission are
assembled together in Roethlisberger, *Claude
drawings*, 1070–74. They are all dated 1674
and are more concerned with the disposition
of the figures than with the composition of
the landscape. The Teyler drawing, doubtless
made six years later, corresponds more closely
with the picture in the main lines of the
composition, though it differs in certain
respects, showing the mere skeleton of the
landscape without the closely observed
details which enrich the painting.

109 Landscape by a lake or river. Inscribed
on the verso in the artist's hand *CLAUDIO IVF*

Black chalk and pale brown wash, strengthened
in the foreground with the pen and grey
wash, 247 × 354 mm.
Inv. no. L.59
Provenance Possibly Queen Christina, etc.
(see van Regteren Altena, p. 22).
Bibliography Scholten, p. 12, L.59;
Roethlisberger, *Claude drawings*, p. 372,
no. 999.

Roethlisberger dates the drawing about 1670,
partly on the evidence of the shaky handwriting on the back, which is typical of
Claude's late years, and partly on the basis of
a comparison with other drawings that can
confidently be dated late. The most arresting
thing about the drawing is the way the artist
has brought the foreground into focus,
revealing the texture of the tree trunks and
the outlines of the leaves and rushes with the
clarity of a lens, while leaving the more
distant shore hazily indistinct. This device,
which exploits the contrast between heavy,
serried pen strokes and faint touches of chalk
and wash is used in several late drawings of
Claude's, but nowhere does it induce so
potent a sense of recession and of mysterious
depths as here. One of the two figures at the
water's edge holds a large fish in his arms and
is sometimes identified as Tobias, wrongly,
according to Roethlisberger.

Antoine Watteau

Painter and engraver. Born Valenciennes,
1684; died Nogent-sur-Marne, 1721.

110 Seated pierrot.
Red chalk heightened with white on buff

Antoine Watteau

paper; the head, collar and trousers touched with black chalk, 242 × 160 mm.
Inv. no. M.20
Exhibitions Amsterdam, Museum Willet-Holthuysen, 1935, 'Antoine Watteau als Teekenaar' (no. 11); Paris and Amsterdam, 1964, no. 50, plate 37.
Bibliography Scholten, p. 23, M.50; Parker and Mathey, Vol. 2, p. 325, no. 649.
Engraved by Boucher (*Figures de différents caractères de paysages et d'études*, plate 119).

111 Standing pierrot.
Red and black chalk heightened with white on grey brown paper, 243 × 158 mm.
Inv. no. M.16
Exhibitions Amsterdam, Rijksmuseum, 1926, 'Exposition rétrospective d'art français', no. 204; Amsterdam, Museum Willet-Holthuysen, 1935, 'Jean Antoine Watteau als Teekenaar', no. 10.
Bibliography Scholten, p. 22, M.16; J. P. Bremmer, *Beeldende Kunst*, Vol. 6, 1918–19, no. 42; *Parker and Mathey*, Vol. 2, p. 326, no. 659.

The figure was used by Watteau in the painting 'Le bal champêtre' (Adhémar, no. 131; Dacier and Vuaflart, Vol. 4, plate 311). A similar figure, with differences, was used in the picture 'Les habits sont italiens' (Adhémar, no. 155; Dacier and Vuaflart, Vol. 4, plate 130). Approximately the same figure was used by a follower of Watteau in the picture 'Gilles, Scaramouche, Scapin and Harlequin' (Adhémar, 245; reproduced in E. H. Zimmermann, *Watteau* (Klassiker der Kunst), Stuttgart, 1912, plate 157). The drawing was engraved by Boucher (*Figures de différents caractères de paysages et d'études*, plate 17).

112 River landscape with church spire.
Inscribed by the artist against the spire *demi teinte grise et généralement les ombres grises.*
The buildings drawn in red chalk, with wash. The rest drawn with brush and watercolour, 160 × 220 mm.
Inv. no. M.15
Exhibitions Paris and Amsterdam, 1964, no. 45.
Bibliography Scholten, p. 22, M.15; K. T. Parker, 'Sidelights on Watteau', in *O.M.D.*, Vol. 10, June 1935, p. 6, plate 4; J. Mathey, 'A landscape of Watteau' in the *Burlington Magazine*, Vol. 89, 1947, pp. 273–74; Parker and Mathey, Vol. 1, p. XIII, p. 63, no. 472, fig. 472.

The church is probably that of Gentilly on the Bièvre. It can be seen again in the painting of La Marmotte in the Hermitage, Leningrad (for an engraving by B. Audran, see Dacier and Vuaflart, Vol. 4, fig. 122; see also Adhémar, plate 6); and again in a landscape in oils in a private collection illustrated in Mathey's article, plate Ia. Watteau made a number of drawings of the valley of the Bièvre and of the town of Gentilly, where his friend Jean de Julienne lived.

On the verso Sketches (3) of an old man and of a hurdy-gurdy player, described in Parker and Mathey, p. 10, no. 53, fig. 53. These scholars regard it as an early drawing under the influence of Gillot, whereas they are inclined to think that the landscape on the recto is a work of the artist's maturity. (See *op. cit.*, p. XIII.) The verso was the side exhibited at Amsterdam and Paris in 1964.

113 Seated Oriental.
Black and red chalk, 248 × 211 mm.

Antoine Watteau

Jean-Baptiste Oudry

Charles Joseph Natoire

Inv. no. M.21a
Provenance Discovered by MM. Lugt and H. Buisman in 1923 in a folder containing anonymous Italian drawings in the Teyler Museum.
Exhibitions London, 1932, no. 723 (no. 771 in the Commemorative Catalogue, 1933); Amsterdam, Willet-Holthuysen Museum, 1935, 'Watteau als teekenaar', 1935 (no. 16); Paris, Palais National des Arts, 1937, 'Chefs-d'oeuvre de l'art français' (no. 592); Brussels, Rotterdam, Paris, 1949–50, 'De Fouquet à Cézanne' (no. 61); Paris and Amsterdam, 1964, no. 40, plate 35.
Bibliography H. Buisman, in *O.M.D.*, Vol. 4, 1930, pp. 67–8, plate 63; K. T. Parker, *The drawings of Antoine Watteau*, 1931, pp. 16, 20 and 49; catalogue and plate no. 99; J. Mathey, 'Remarques sur la chronologie des peintres et dessins d'Antoine Watteau', in *Bulletin de la Société de l'histoire de l'art français*, 1939, pp. 158–59; Parker and Mathey, Vol. 2, no. 791.

The sitter was probably one of the retinue of the Persian ambassador Riza Bey, who came to Paris in 1715 and was received by Louis XIV in the Gallérie des Glaces at Versailles, a ceremony recorded in two pictures by Antoine Coypel, the one at Versailles, the other in the Museum at Saintes. Ten other drawings of members of the Persian embassy by Watteau are known, including one in the Victoria and Albert Museum and another sheet in the Teyler Museum (Parker and Mathey, Vol. 2, nos. 790–801). None of them was used in a painting, as far as is known. The Teyler drawing was engraved by Boucher (*Figures de différents caractères de paysages et d'études*, plate 156).

Jean-Baptiste Oudry

Painter. Born Paris, 1686; died there, 1755.

114 A wolf at bay.

Pen and black ink and brown wash over red chalk, squared in red chalk, 387 × 534 mm.
Inv. no. U.*55
Provenance Miss B. G. Roelofs, sale 2 April 1873, no. 74; bought by Gruyter for fl. 13.50 for the Teyler Foundation.
Bibliography Scholten, p. 412, U.*55.

It is a carefully finished design for a painting, signed and dated 1722, in the Schlossgalerie in Ansbach (see Jan Lauts, *Jean-Baptiste Oudry*, Hamburg and Berlin, 1967, p. 25, plate 4). The drawing corresponds closely with the picture.

Charles Joseph Natoire

Painter and etcher. Born Nîmes, 1700; died Castelgandolfo, 1777.

115 The Adoration of the Shepherds.

Signed *C. Natoire* and dated *1764*.
Red and black chalk, strengthened in black ink, with brown and grey washes, 208 × 165 mm.
Inv. no. M.29
Bibliography Scholten, p. 25, M.29; F. Boyer, *Catalogue raisonné de l'oeuvre de Charles Natoire* in *Archives de l'Art Français*, 1949, p. 76, no. 349.

Presumably made in Italy, where Natoire was Director of the French Academy in Rome (since 1751). Boyer lists no picture of this subject among the artist's surviving works.

François Boucher

Hubert Robert

François Boucher

Painter and engraver. Born Paris, 1703; died there, 1770.

116 Jacob and Rachel at the Well
(Genesis XXIX, 10).
Pen with some touches of wash over a slight sketch in black chalk, 230 × 289 mm.
Inv. no. M.31
Exhibition Amsterdam, Rijksmuseum, 1926, Exhibition of French art, no. 119.
Bibliography Scholten, p. 25, M.31; A. Ananoff, *L'oeuvre dessiné de François Boucher*, Paris, 1966, p. 183, no. 694.

Old Testament subjects are uncommon in Boucher's oeuvre; so are pen drawings; but the handling is typical of Boucher. No record has been found of a picture on the theme of Jacob and Rachel; but the drawing is evidently a compositional study for a picture or engraved illustration.

117 Two figures in oriental dress; a boy standing and singing or reciting, with a sleeping man.
Pen and wash, 202 × 138 mm.
Bibliography Scholten, p. 26, no. M.33.

Hubert Robert

Painter and etcher. Born Paris, 1733; died there, 1808.

118 A Doric temple in ruins with a peasant family camping beside it. Signed and dated on the pedestal on the left *H. Roberti Roma invenit 1761.*
Pen and brown wash and watercolour, 260 × 328 mm.
Inv. no. M.38
Bibliography Scholten, p. 27, M.38.

Robert had made a tour of Naples and its surroundings as far as Paestum in 1760. This drawing is probably a reminiscence of that journey.

List of books referred to in abbreviated form

Adhémar	J. Adhémar, *Watteau*, Paris, 1960.
Barocchi	P. Barocchi. *Michelangelo e la sua scuola. I disegni di Casa Buonarroti e degli Uffizi*, Florence, 1962.
Bartsch	A. Bartsch, *Le peintre-graveur*, Vols. 1–21, Vienna, 1803–21.
Benesch	O. Benesch, *The drawings of Rembrandt*, 6 vols., London, 1954–57.
Berenson	B. Berenson, *The drawings of the Florentine painters*, amplified edition, Chicago, 1938. The references are to Vol. 3, *Catalogue*. An Italian edition was published in Milan, 1961. The catalogue nos. are the same. It is not quoted in the bibliography unless a change of view is expressed.
Berenson, *Venetian School*	B. Berenson, *Italian pictures of the Renaissance. Venetian School*. London, 1957.
Bernt	W. Bernt, *Die niederländischen Zeichner des 17. Jahrhunderts*, 2 vols., Munich, 1957.
Briganti	G. Briganti, *Pietro da Cortona o della pittura barocca*, Florence, 1962.
Brinckmann	A. E. Brinckmann, *Michelangelo-Zeichnungen*, Munich, 1925.
Buisman	H. Buisman, *Teyler's Museum Haarlem. Veertig Teekeningen van oude meesters der hollandsche schoolen enkele der vlaamsche*, Leipzig, 1924.
Chiarini	M. Chiarini, *Claude Lorrain. Selected drawings*, University Park, U.S.A., and London, 1968.
Crowe	J. A. Crowe and G. B. Cavalcaselle, *Raphael: his life and works*, 2 vols., London, 1882.
Dacier and Vuaflart	E. Dacier and A. Vuaflart, *Jean de Julienne et les graveurs de Watteau au 18ᵉ siècle*, 4 vols., Paris, 1922.
Delacre	M. Delacre, *Le dessin de Michel-Ange*, Brussels, 1938.
Dollmayr	H. Dollmayr, 'Raffaels Werkstatt' in *Jahrbuch der Kunsthistorischen Sammlungen des allerhöchsten Kaiserhauses*, Vol. 16, 1895, pp. 231 ff.
Dussler	L. Dussler, *Die Zeichnungen des Michelangelo*, Berlin, 1959.
Dussler, *Raphael*	L. Dussler, *Raffael. Kritisches Verzeichnis der Gemälde, Wandbilder und Bildteppiche*, Munich, 1966.
Fairfax Murray Cat.	*A selection from the collection of drawings by the old masters formed by C. Fairfax Murray*, London, [1905].

Fischel, *Versuch*	O. Fischel *Raphaels Zeichnungen. Versuch einer Kritik der bisher veröffentlichten Blätter*, Strassburg, 1898.
Frey	K. Frey, *Die Handzeichnungen Michelagniolos Buonarroti*, 3 vols., Berlin, 1909–11.
Goldscheider, 1951	L. Goldscheider, *Michelangelo drawings*, London, 1951.
Goldscheider, 1966	The second edition of the same book.
Haendcke	B. Haendcke, '*Zu Michelangelos Zeichnungen in Haarlem*', in *Repertorium für Kunstwissenschaft*, Vol. 24, 1901, pp. 387–89.
H.d.G.	C. Hofstede de Groot, *A catalogue raisonné of the works of the most eminent Dutch painters of the seventeenth century, based on the work of John Smith*, English edition, 8 vols., London, 1907–27.
Hind, *Claude drawings*	A. M. Hind, *The drawings of Claude Lorrain*, London, 1925.
Hind, *Claude drawings in B.M.*	A. M. Hind, *British Museum. Catalogue of the drawings of Claude Lorrain*, London, 1926.
Hind, *Dutch and Flemish Catalogue*	A. M. Hind, *Catalogue of drawings by Dutch and Flemish artists preserved in the Department of Prints and Drawings in the British Museum*, 5 vols., London, 1915–32.
Hind, *Rembrandt*	A. M. Hind, *A catalogue of Rembrandt's etchings*, 2 vols., London, 1912.
Hollstein	F. W. H. Hollstein, *Dutch and Flemish etchings, engravings and woodcuts ca. 1450–1700*, 15 vols. so far published, Amsterdam, c. 1949–64.
Kitson	M. Kitson, *Claude's books of drawings from Nature*, in *Burlington Magazine*, Vol. 103, 1961, pp. 252–57.
Knapp	F. Knapp. *Die Handzeichnungen Michelagniolos Buonarroti. Nachtrag zu den von Karl Frey herausgegebenen drei Bänden*, Berlin, 1925.
Lugt	F. Lugt, *Les marques de collections de dessins et d'estampes*, Amsterdam, 1921 and *Supplément*, The Hague, 1956.
Lugt, *Flemish drawings*	F. Lugt, *Musée du Louvre. Inventaire général des dessins des écoles du Nord. École flamande*, 2 vols., Paris, 1949.
Marcuard	F. V. Marcuard, *Die Zeichnungen Michelangelos im Museum Teyler zu Haarlem*, Munich, 1901.
Nagler	G. K. Nagler. *Neues allgemeines Künstler-Lexicon*, 22 vols., Munich, 1835–52.
O.M.D.	*Old master drawings. A quarterly magazine for students and collectors.* Vols. 1–14, London, 1926–40.
Panofsky	E. Panofsky, 'Bemerkungen zu der Neuherausgabe der Haarlemer Michelangelo-Zeichnungen durch Fr. Knapp', in *Repertorium für Kunstwissenschaft*, Vol. 48, Berlin-Leipzig, 1927, pp. 25–58.
Parker	K. T. Parker, *Catalogue of the collection of drawings in the Ashmolean Museum, Volume II. Italian schools*, Oxford, 1956.

Parker and Mathey	K. T. Parker and J. Mathey, *Catalogue de l'oeuvre dessiné d'Antoine Watteau*, Paris, 1957.
Passavant	J. D. Passavant, *Raphael d'Urbin et son père Giovanni Santi . . . Édition française . . . revue et annotée par M. Paul Lacroix*, 2 vols., Paris, 1860.
Popham and Pouncey	A. E. Popham and P. Pouncey, *Italian drawings in the Department of prints and drawings in the British Museum. The fourteenth and fifteenth centuries*, 2 vols., London, 1950.
Popham and Wilde	A. E. Popham and J. Wilde, *The Italian drawings of the XV and XVI centuries in the collection of His Majesty the King at Windsor Castle*, London, 1949.
Pouncey and Gere	P. Pouncey and J. A. Gere, *Italian drawings in the Department of Prints and Drawings in the British Museum. Raphael and his circle*, London, 1962.
Prussian Jahrbuch	*Jahrbuch der Königlich Preussischen Kunstsammlungen*, Vols. 1–64, Berlin, 1880–1943 (from 1919 'Königlich' is omitted).
Reznicek	E. K. J. Reznicek, *Die Zeichnungen von Hendrick Goltzius*, 2 vols., Utrecht, 1961.
Roethlisberger, *Claude drawings*	M. Roethlisberger, *Claude Lorrain: The drawings*, 2 vols., Berkeley and Los Angeles, 1968.
Roethlisberger, *Claude paintings*	M. Roethlisberger, *Claude Lorrain: The paintings*, 2 vols., New Haven, 1961.
Scholten	H. J. Scholten, *Musée Teyler à Haarlem. Catalogue raisonné des dessins des écoles françaises et hollandaises*, Haarlem, 1904.
Stechow	W. Stechow, 'Daniele da Volterra als Bildhauer' in *Jahrbuch der preussischen Kunstsammlungen*, Vol. 49, 1928, pp. 82 ff.
Thode	H. Thode, *Michelangelo. Kritische Untersuchungen über seine Werke*, 3 vols., Berlin, 1908–13.
Tietze	H. Tietze and E. Tietze-Conrat, *The drawings of the Venetian painters in the fifteenth and sixteenth centuries*, New York, 1944.
Tolnay	C. de Tolnay, *Michelangelo*, 5 vols., Princeton, 1943–60.
van Regteren Altena	J. Q. van Regteren Altena, *Les dessins italiens de la Reine Christine de Suède (Analecta Reginensia II)*, Stockholm, 1966.
Venturi	A. Venturi. *Storia dell'arte italiana* (XI vols., from VI onwards subdivided into parts), Milan, 1901–39.
Vienna Jahrbuch	*Jahrbuch der Kunsthistorischen Sammlungen des allerhöchsten Kaiserhauses*, Vienna, 1883–1918. (*Jahrbuch der Kunsthistorischen Sammlungen in Wien* from 1919.)
Wilde. *BM Catalogue*	J. Wilde. *Italian drawings in the British Museum, Michelangelo and his studio*, London, 1953.
Wölfflin	H. Wölfflin. Review of Marcuard in *Repertorium für Kunstwissenschaft*, Vol. 24, 1901.

List of exhibitions referred to in abbreviated form

in alphabetical order

Amsterdam, 1932	Rembrandt tentoonstelling ter plechtige herdenking van het 300 – jarig bestaan der Universiteit van Amsterdam; in the Rijksmuseum.
Amsterdam, 1934	Italiaansche Kunst in Nederlandsch Bezit; in the Stedelijk Museum.
Amsterdam, 1955	De Triomf van het maniërisme – de Europeesche stijl van Michelangelo tot el Greco; in the Rijksmuseum.
Amsterdam, 1956	Rembrandt tentoonstelling ter herdenking van de geboorte van Rembrandt op 15 Juli 1606; in the Rijksmuseum, Amsterdam, and the Museum Boymans, Rotterdam.
Brussels, 1937–38	De Jérome Bosch à Rembrandt. Dessins hollandais du XVIe au XVIIe siècles; in the Palais des Beaux-Arts.
Brussels, 1961	Hollandse tekeningen uit de gouden eeuw; in the Albert I Library. There is also a French edition of the catalogue, 1961.
Goltzius, Rotterdam – Haarlem, 1958	H. Goltzius als tekenaar; in the Museum Boymans, Rotterdam, and the Teyler Museum, Haarlem.
Haarlem, 1951	Rembrandt tentoonstelling – teekeningen en etsen; in the Vleeshal.
London, 1929	Exhibition of Dutch Art; in the Royal Academy of Arts, Burlington House. Commemorative Catalogue, Oxford, 1930.
London, 1930	Exhibition of Italian Art; in the Royal Academy, Burlingon House.
London, 1932	French Art, 1200–1900; in the Royal Academy, Burlington House.
Paris, 1921	Exposition hollandaise: tableaux, aquarelles et dessins anciens et modernes, in the Musée du Louvre.
Paris, 1950	Le paysage hollandais au XVIIe siècle; in the Orangerie.
Paris and Amsterdam, 1964	Le dessin français de Claude à Cézanne dans les collections hollandaises; at the Institut Néerlandais, Paris, and in the Rijksmuseum, Amsterdam.
Paris, Rotterdam, Haarlem, 1962	Le dessin italien dans les collections hollandaises; in the Institut Néerlandais, Paris, the Boymans Museum, Rotterdam, and the Teyler Museum, Haarlem.
Saenredam, Amsterdam, 1938	Pieter Jansz Saenredam, Schilderijen en teekeningen; in the Museum Fodor.

Saenredam, Rotterdam, 1937   Pieter Jansz Saenredam, Schilderijen en teekeningen; in the Boymans Museum.

Saenredam, Utrecht, 1961   Catalogue raisonné van de werken van Pieter Jansz. Saenredam, uitgegeven ter gelegenheid van de tentoonstelling P. J. Saenredam; in the Centraal Museum.
There exists a revised English edition of the catalogue, 1961.

Stockholm, 1966   Christina, Queen of Sweden; in the National Museum.

Utrecht, 1953   Nederlandse Architectuur schilders, 1600–1900; in the Centraal Museum.

Van Dijck, Antwerp, 1949   Van Dijck tentoonstelling; in the Palais des Beaux-Arts.

Washington, etc., 1958–59   Dutch drawings – Masterpieces of five centuries; in the National Gallery of Art, Washington, the Pierpont Morgan Library, New York, the Minneapolis Institute of Arts, the Museum of Fine Arts, Boston, the Cleveland Museum of Art, and the Art Institute of Chicago.

Index of artists
The references are to the catalogue numbers

Plates

1 Paulus Bril
Italian landscape

3 Hendrick Goltzius
   Saint Cecilia

4 Hendrick Goltzius
  Antique marble candelabrum

5 Hendrick Goltzius
   Mountain landscape

6 Hendrick Goltzius
   Female nude

26 Jan Lievens
Portrait of de le Boe Sylvius

27 Jan Asselijn
   Bas-relief on the arch of Titus

34 Philips de Koninck
   Landscape

A·van de Velde·f·

48 Adriaen van de Velde
    Pastoral scene

49 Caspar Netcher
A young lady embroidering

57 Jacob de Wit
A cherub's head

59 Aert Schouman
Birds in a park

60 Jurriaen Andriessen
Arcadian landscape

61 Wybrand Hendriks
   Head of a wild boar

63 Anonymous. Lombard School;
   late fourteenth century
   A greyhound

64 Anonymous. North Italian; about 1400
Allegorical figure

70 Michelangelo
Male nude

71 Michelangelo
The Descent from the Cross

73 Michelangelo
  Studies of Christ on the Cross

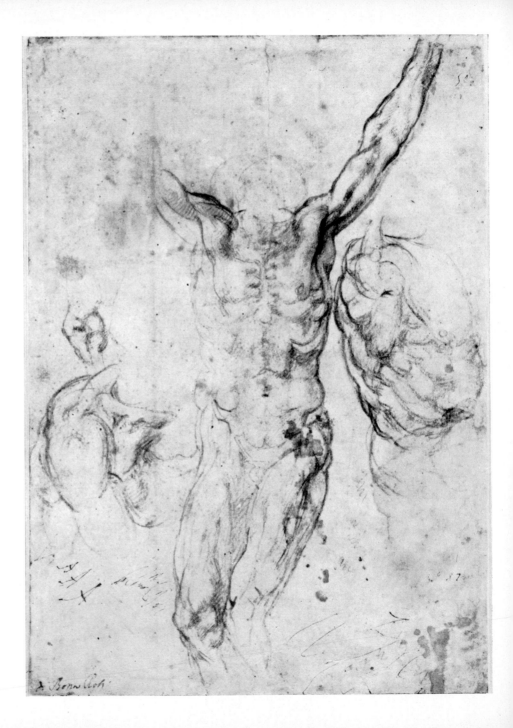

75 Daniele da Volterra
   Portrait of Michelangelo

76 Raphael
A putto

80 Giulio Romano
   Neptune

81 Giulio Romano
   The Gonzaga arms

82 Correggio
   Study for Eve

83a, b and c. Attributed to Schiavone
   Three standing figures

88 Pietro Facini
     St. Francis

89 Attributed to Guido Reni
   Figure study

90 Domenichino
   Head of an old man

91 Giovanni Lanfranco
  Two reclining goddesses

92 Giovanni Lanfranco
    Allegorical figure

93 Guercino
Studies of St. John the Evangelist

96 Pietro da Cortona
   Ceiling design

97 School of Pietro da Cortona
Birth of the Virgin

98 Anonymous. Roman School;
   mid–seventeenth century
   The Mocking of Christ

99 Gianlorenzo Bernini
    An allegory of Christ's Blood

101 Pietro Testa
   Study for figures in a pendentive

102 Bartolomeo Biscaino
Virgin and Child

110 Antoine Watteau
   Seated pierrot

113 Antoine Watteau
   Seated oriental

115 Charles Joseph Natoire
The Adoration of the Shepherds